COLLINS GEM
CATS

a mine of information

COLLINS GEM
Chinese

COLLINS GEM
Classic
BOOKS

COLLINS GEM
Classic
FILMS

a mine of information

COLLINS G
HORS!
& PONIES

a mine of information

COLLINS GEM
**OMS
OOLS**

a mine of information

COLLINS GEM
SNAKES

a mine of information

COLLINS GEM
SPIDERS

a mine of information

COLLINS GEM
STRESS
Survival Guide

a mine of information

COLLINS GEM
TAROT

a mine of information

COLLINS GEM
WINE
Guide

a mine of information

COLLINS GEM
WORLD
atlas

a mine of information

COLLINS GEM
YOGA

a mine of information

COLLINS GEM
ZODIAC
Types

a mine of information

CHEMICAL ELEMENTS

Gerard Cheshire

**Consultant:
Professor Peter Day FRS**

HarperCollins*Publishers*

Gerard Cheshire is a science writer, living in Bath. He became BSc at University College London and MSc at the University of Bristol. He has written on a wide variety of scientific subjects including anthropology and ecology and land management for many well-known publishers.

Professor Peter Day FRS has been a University Lecturer and Ad Hominem Professor of Solid State Chemistry at Oxford and Tutor to St John's College, to which he was elected Honorary Fellow. He was elected Fellow of the Royal Society in 1986. In 1989 he became Director of the Institut Laue-Langevin, Grenoble. In 1991 he was appointed director of the Royal Institution and its Davy Faraday Research Laboratory where he became Fullerian Professor of Chemistry. He has received the Corday-Morgan Medal and the Award for Solid State Chemistry from The Royal Society of Chemistry.

Thanks to Douglas Courtney, Claire Dashwood, Dr Mary Harman, Chris Herbert, Nicola Marlin.

HarperCollins *Publishers*
103 Westerhill Road, Bishopbriggs,
Glasgow, G64 2QT
www.collins-gem.com

First published 2001

Reprint 10 9 8 7 6 5 4 3 2 1 0

ISBN 0 00 710935-0

Created and produced by Flame Tree Publishing, part of The Foundry Creative Media Co. Ltd, Crabtree Hall, Crabtree Lane, London SW6 6TY

Printed in Italy by Amadeus S.p.A

Contents

INTRODUCTION
What is an Element?

THE THEORY THAT everything in the universe is made up of hundreds of millions of tiny particles was first put forward by the Ancient Greek philosopher Democritus (*c.* 460–361 BC). It took hundreds of years and huge scientific advances to really explore and understand this theory. It was the English chemist

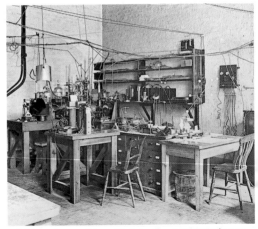

In laboratories around the world, nineteenth-century scientists began to try to answer the question 'What is an element?'

John Dalton (1766–1844) who expanded and advanced the early theories when he put forward his atomic theory of matter in 1808. Dalton's work stated that all matter is made up of tiny particles called atoms which cannot be split into anything smaller – although this was later proved to be incorrect. A group of identical atoms form an element. An element is therefore a substance that cannot be broken down into a more simple substance by any chemical reaction as it is composed of only one type of atoms. Dalton stated that all atoms of one element are alike and that the individual chemical elements differ from one another because the atoms from which they are made differ slightly – i.e. all hydrogen atoms are the same but hydrogen has different properties to helium because helium and hydrogen are made up from slightly different atoms; a gold bar is made up of only one kind of atom: gold atoms. Dalton's work forms the basis of our current understanding of what an element is.

Mass number = Number of protons plus the number of neutrons in the nucleus of an atom. Written at the top left of the symbol (see page 9).

Symbol = Abbreviation for Common or Latin name.

Atomic number = Number of protons in the nucleus of an atom. Written at the bottom left of the symbol (see page 9).

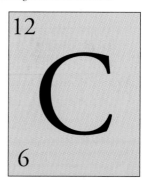

What are Atoms Made of?

FOLLOWING work on various early atomic models by J. J. Thompson (1856–1940) and Ernest Rutherford (1871–1937) – each of which had their individual failings – Rutherford proposed his nuclear model of 1911. According to Rutherford, there was a positively charged central nucleus around which orbited the negatively charged electrons. Rutherford proposed his nuclear model to explain the results of work carried out by Hans Wilhelm Geiger (1882–1945) and Marsden. The scattering experiments they carried out showed that most positively charged alpha-particles passed straight through a sheet of gold foil, but a tiny percentage were deflected. Rutherford explained this by proposing that as most of the atom was empty space they passed straight through but the presence of a solid, positively charged nucleus was proved by the fact that some deflection occurred. The positively charged alpha-particles were being repelled by the positive nuclei in the gold. Following Rutherford's work it was widely accepted that the centre of the atom contained a positively charged nucleus of massive proportions compared to the negatively charged electrons.

PROTONS AND NEUTRONS IN THE NUCLEUS

THE SUB-ATOMIC particles in the nucleus that gave it its positive charge were named protons. It was assumed at this stage that protons were the only particles in the nucleus – that is until studies were carried out on hydrogen and helium. These showed that the helium nucleus had twice the charge, but four times the mass of a hydrogen nucleus. Therefore something else had to exist

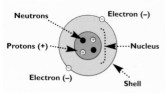

Neutrons
Electron (–)
Protons (+)
Nucleus
Electron (–)
Shell

A Helium Atom has a nucleus and a single shell. The nucleus contains two protons and two neutrons and is orbited by two electrons

in the nucleus, contributing to the mass but not to the charge. These uncharged particles were named neutrons.

The number of protons is specific to an element – if the number of protons change, then the nucleus becomes that of a different element: hydrogen has one proton, helium has two, lithium has three and so on. As the number of protons is specific for each element, the number of protons is used as a descriptor of the element – the so-called atomic number. The mass of an electron is almost zero, but neutrons and protons are relatively heavy, and of equal mass.

The number of neutrons in an element's nucleus can vary. Changes in the number of neutrons in an atom's nucleus changes the mass of the atom, but it is still the same element. Thus a nucleus with six protons is carbon, if it has seven it is nitrogen. However, a nucleus with six protons can have six or eight neutrons making it either carbon-12 or carbon-14. An element's unique atomic number is therefore the number of protons in the nucleus. Isotopes of an element have the same number of protons but a different numbers of neutrons. ^{12}C and ^{14}C are the same element but ^{12}C has six neutrons, ^{14}C has eight. Isotopes of uranium have a different number of neutrons but are the same element. When ^{238}U decays it produces thorium, a completely different element. The mass number of an element is the number of protons and neutrons found in the nucleus of one of its atoms.

ELECTRONS AND SHELLS

99.9% OF AN atom is empty space occupied by electrons moving in rapid orbits, or shells, around the nucleus. Some atoms, such as helium, only have one shell, whereas others, such as calcium, have several shells.

It is the electrons in the outer shell that determine an atom's chemical behaviour. If the outer shell is complete with the maximum number of electrons it can hold, it does not need to bond with any other elements to fill the outer shell. An element with a complete outer shell is very stable. Argon, for example, has a full outer shell, is stable and does not form chemical bonds.

An atom that does not have a complete outer shell, i.e. does not contain the maximum number of electrons that it can, is not stable. The atom is reactive as it wants to complete the outer shell and will form a bond with another atom to achieve this. The number of such bonds that an atom can form is its valency.

	First Shell	Second shell (2)		Third shell (3)		
		sub-shells 2s 2p		sub-shells 3s 3p 3d		
18 Argon	2	2	6	2	6	

Argon, with an atomic number of 18, has 18 electrons in three shells. The second and third shells are divided into the sub-shells s and p. Two other types of sub-shell exist, the d and f shells.

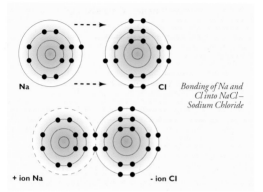

Bonding of Na and Cl into NaCl – Sodium Chloride

The example of sodium and chlorine will help explain this. A sodium atom has eleven electrons altogether, two in its first shell, eight in its second shell, leaving one in its outer shell. To be stable it needs to lose the electron in its outer shell. Chlorine has seventeen electrons in total, seven in its outer shell, so to be stable it needs to gain one electron to have a complete outside shell. If one electron is transferred from a sodium atom to a chlorine atom then both elements have achieved a full complement of eight electrons in their outer shells. Both elements have a valency of one. An ionic bond is formed between the two atoms, now called ions, leading to the formation of the ionic compound sodium chloride. The elements grouped together in the periodic table have atoms with the same number of electrons in their outside shells therefore, within these groups, the elements will react with other elements in similar ways.

RELATIVE ATOMIC MASS (RAM)

IN 1858 Stanislao Cannizzaro (1826–1910), published a list of fixed atomic weights, now known as relative atomic masses (RAM) for the 60 elements that were known at the time. When arranged by increasing RAM it was noticed that similarities in terms of chemical properties occurred at regular intervals. It was not until Dmitri Mendeleyev (1834–1907) arranged the elements in rows in order of their RAM, and placed elements that behaved in similar ways below each other, however, that the modern periodic table was invented.

Carbon was chosen as the 'standard' for the calculation of RAM. Carbon-12 atoms were given a RAM of 12 and the relative masses of other atoms are obtained by comparison with the mass of a carbon atom. For example, carbon atoms are 12 times as heavy as hydrogen atoms; therefore hydrogen has a RAM of one. Oxygen is 16 times as heavy as hydrogen so has a RAM of 16.

Moles

RAM is important in the study of compounds. By dividing the mass of an element by its RAM we discover how many moles there are in a sample. A mole is an SI unit, defined as the number of carbon atoms in 12 g of the isotope carbon-12. It has a value of 6×10^{23}. A mole of any substance will contain 6×10^{23} particles of that substance. This is very important in chemical reactions where you need exact proportions of atoms. The weight of a mole of a substance is equal to the element's RAM.

Radioactivity

THE ATOMS of an element have a specific number of protons. Most atoms have stable nuclei where the number of protons and neutrons stay the same. However, some nuclei are not stable and can split up. Atoms with unstable nuclei are radioactive. Radioactive decay is the breaking up of nuclei with the release of energy.

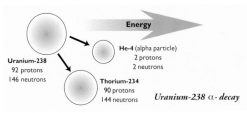

Energy

He-4 (alpha particle)
2 protons
2 neutrons

Uranium-238
92 protons
146 neutrons

Thorium-234
90 protons
144 neutrons

Uranium-238 α- decay

In α-radioactivity, uranium-238 loses energy and two protons and two neutrons (as a helium-4 nucleus) and therefore becomes thorium-234.

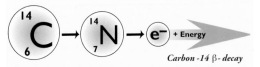

Carbon -14 β- decay

In β-radioactivity, carbon-14 has one neutron that becomes a proton giving nitrogen-14, with the emission of an electron (a beta particle).

The larger the number of subatomic particles in an atom, the more likely it is that they will be radioactive. There are three types of radiation: alpha (α), beta (β) and gamma (γ). Large atoms decay by emitting α-radiation. Beta radiation occurs when there is an unequal number of protons and neutrons and can occur in all elements. The third type, γ-radiation, is the most dangerous and results in a more stable form of the element. Bismuth has an atomic number of 83 and this marks the upper limit of the number of protons there can be for an element to be stable. All the elements with an atomic number higher than bismuth are radioactive.

HALF-LIFE

THE RATE of radioactive decay is measured as half-life: the time it takes for half the radioactive nuclei in a radioactive substance to decay. The half-life of uranium-238 is 4.5 billion years; it takes this long for half of the radioactive nuclei in any amount of ^{238}U to decay radioactively. Decay continues until a stable state is reached. Uranium decays to form lead. Looking at the periodic table we see that uranium, atomic number 92, decays into thorium, atomic number 90. If we follow this pattern we see that it then forms radium (88), radon (86), polonium (84) then lead (82). It stops at lead as this is the first element with an atomic number lower than that of bismuth (83) – 83 being the limit of the number of protons there can be for an element to be stable. Isotopes with long half-lives are more stable than those which decay rapidly.

Some of elements, e.g. thorium, decay so slowly that natural deposits occur. Other elements, such as 114 (ununquadium) and 116 (ununhexium) are so reactive that they have only been artificially produced for milliseconds before decaying.

Explanation of the Periodic Table

MENDELEYEV'S PERIODIC TABLE

IN 1869 Dmitri Mendeleyev (1834–1907) published his version of the periodic table, on which all present-day versions are based. The periodic table is a diagrammatic representation of all the known elements ordered in a specific way. Important information can be obtained about any element just by looking at its position in the table relative to others.

Mendeleyev organised the elements in the periodic table by placing them in order of their relative atomic masses (RAM). He wrote the elements in a series of horizontal rows (periods) so that the elements with similar properties appeared in the same vertical columns (groups). To make sure elements with the same properties were in the same group Mendeleyev sometimes had to leave gaps. The table was still informative as it enabled scientists to predict the properties of the missing elements. Mendeleyev's assumptions as to the properties of these missing elements proved to be remarkably accurate.

Dmitri Mendeleyev.

Periodic

Group	I 1	II 2		3	4	5	6	7	8
Period									
1	H 1								
2	Li 3	Be 4							
3	Na 11	Mg 12							
4	K 19	Ca 20		Sc 21	Ti 22	V 23	Cr 24	Mn 25	Fe 26
5	Rb 37	Sr 38		Y 39	Zr 40	Nb 41	Mo 42	Tc 43	Ru 44
6	Cs 55	Ba 56		57 – 71*	Hf 72	Ta 73	W 74	Re 75	Os 76
7	Fr 87	Ra 88		89 – 103**	Rf 104	Db 105	Sg 106	Bh 107	Hs 108

*Lanthanides	La 57	Ce 58	Pr 59	Nd 60	Pm 61	Sm 62
**Actinides	Ac 89	Th 90	Pa 91	U 92	Np 93	Pu 94

Note that elements 113, 115 and 117 are not yet known, but are included in the table to show their respective positions. Elements 114, 116 and 118 have only been reported recently.

Table

				III 13	IV 14	V 15	VI 16	VII 17	O 18
9	10	11	12	13	14	15	16	17	18
									He 2
				B 5	C 6	N 7	O 8	F 9	Ne 10
				Al 13	Si 14	P 15	S 16	Cl 17	Ar 18
Co 27	Ni 28	Cu 29	Zn 30	Ga 31	Ge 32	As 33	Se 34	Br 35	Kr 36
Rh 45	Pd 46	Ag 47	Cd 48	In 49	Sn 50	Sb 51	Te 52	I 53	Xe 54
Ir 77	Pt 78	Au 79	Hg 80	Tl 81	Pb 82	Bi 83	Po 84	At 85	Rn 86
Mt 109	Uun 110	Uuu 111	Uub 112	Uut 113	Uuq 114	Uup 115	Uuh 116	Uus 117	Uuo 118

Eu 63	Gd 64	Tb 65	Dy 66	Ho 67	Er 68	Tm 69	Yb 70	Lu 71
Am 95	Cm 96	Bk 97	Cf 98	Es 99	Fm 100	Md 101	No 102	Lr 103

Key: ▢ Non-metal ▢ Metalloid ▢ Metal ▢ Transitional ▢ Rare-earth element (Lanthanide) and radioactive rare-earth element (Actinide) ▢ Transactinide ▢ 'Missing' element

PROPERTIES OF ELEMENTS

MOVING from left to right across the table, the elements change from metals to non-metals. As you move from the top of each group towards the bottom there is a gradual change in the elements' properties. The groups are numbered across the top of the periodic table but some groups also have names: group I are the alkali metals, group II the alkaline-earth metals, in the middle of the table, starting in period 4, the groups contain the transitional elements, group VII contains the halogens and group 0, the final column, the noble gases. The elements in the top right-hand side of the periodic table are the non-metals. Elements that fall close to the division of the metals and non-metals are called the metalloids. The elements get more reactive the closer they are to the right or left edges of the table, excluding those in group 0, the noble gases. Therefore the most reactive elements are in group I, they are less reactive in group II, with the transitional elements being even less reactive. The most reactive non-metals are the halogens which are in the last group of the table, group VII, before the unreactive noble gases. Within the groups the elements share properties which characterise them:

Metals: Most of the elements are metals. Most metals, apart from mercury, are usually shiny solids at room temperature. They conduct heat and electricity well and usually have high melting and boiling points. Most are malleable.

Non-metals: Most of the non-metals, located to the top right of the table, are gases at room temperature and have low melting and boiling points. With the exception of carbon they are poor conductors. Non-metals are soft and brittle, they are not malleable.

Metalloids: These are located next to the division between metals and non-metals in the periodic table. They can be divided into the poor metals and semimetals. The poor metals, such as lead and aluminium, are soft, weak and have comparatively low melting points. Tin and lead were amongst the earliest metals used by man because they melt so easily and are therefore relatively simple to extract from their ores. The semimetals have properties similar to both metals and non-metals. Some look hard, metallic and shiny, like arsenic, but are poor conductors of heat or electricity. The most important use of the semimetals is in semiconductors used for microchips and electronic components.

Alkali metals: The alkali metals are in group I of the table and include elements such as sodium. All the alkali metals react with water to form alkaline solutions. They are all silvery white, are easily cut with a knife and have one electron in their outer shell. They are very reactive and are usually stored under oil to protect them from oxygen and water. The alkali metals get more reactive towards the bottom of the group.

Alkaline-earth metals: The alkaline-earth metals, in group II of the table, react with water to form alkaline solutions and are abundant in nature. They are all silvery white when pure and have two electrons in their outer shell. They are less reactive than alkali metals.

Transition elements: The transition elements, such as iron and copper, are located between the reactive metals in group I and II and the poor metals to the bottom right of the table. The transition elements make up the bulk of the periodic table and they share certain characteristics: they are shiny, hard, strong, have high melting points and are good conductors of heat and electricity. Many of them are good catalysts, form alloys with other metals and have coloured compounds. Unlike other parts of the periodic table, there are similarities across the periods of the transition elements as well as down the group. They are all fairly unreactive and do not react with cold water.

Halogens: All the halogens, found in group VII, are light-sensitive – they are frequently used to make photographic film. They are highly reactive and have seven electrons in their outer shell. They are so reactive that they are never found naturally as uncombined elements but occur with metals in salts, for example sodium chloride or calcium fluoride. Indeed the word halogen means 'salt formers'. In reverse to group I, the halogens get more reactive towards the top of the group.

Noble gases: These are in group 0 at the far right of the periodic table. They were formerly called the inert gases because it was believed they could not form compounds. We now know that a few compounds can be made so they were renamed noble gases. They are unreactive because their outer shells are filled with electrons. They are colourless and odourless at room temperature.

ALLOTROPES

ALLOTROPES are different forms of the same element, for example, diamond and graphite are allotropes of carbon. Although they look completely different, they are both actually carbon. The atoms of carbon in diamond and graphite are arranged differently: in diamond each atom is joined to four others in a lattice; in graphite each carbon atom is attached to only three others and they are arranged in sheets. In 1990 scientists discovered yet another allotrope of carbon which has a molecular structure that resembles a football, or the domed roof of a stadium designed by an American engineer called Richard Buckminster Fuller. This allotrope was named buckminsterfullerene, now popularly known as 'buckyballs', after the architect. The differences in molecular structure are what make these three allotropes of the same element so physically different.

How To Use This Book

This book is organised alphabetically using the common English name of each of the elements in the periodic table. The data boxes at the beginning of each entry include information such as the element's valency, details of its location in the periodic table and its melting and boiling points. Information is also given on the origins of the element's name. For quick reference the element's symbol is clearly presented at the start of the entry. The text provides information on the discovery of the element, its uses, properties and other interesting data.

KEY TO DATA BOXES

Symbol Abbreviation for Common or Latin name.

Atomic Number Number of protons in the nucleus of an atom.

Relative Atomic Mass (RAM) Relative to $^1/_{12}$ of the mass of carbon-12 atom.

Valency A number given to an atom, equal to the number of atoms of hydrogen that it could bond with.

Element Type either gas, liquid non-metal, metal, metalloid or transitional.

Group Vertical column of elements in the periodic table with similar properties

Period Horizontal row of elements in the periodic table with equal numbers of electron shells.

Relative Density (RD) Density relative to water. The relative density of a solid or liquid is calculated with it at 20 °C (68 °F) relative to water at 4 °C (39.2 °F) at average atmospheric pressure at sea level which averages at 101 kilopascals (or 1013 millibars or 760 millimetres of mercury [mmHg] or 14.7 lb/sq in).

The relative density of a gas is calculated relative to the density of hydrogen, or occasionally dry air, at the same temperature and pressure as itself.

Melting or Fusing Point (MP) Temperature at which a solid becomes a liquid or a liquid fuses into a solid.

Boiling Point (BP) Temperature at which a liquid or fused solid turns into to vapour or gas.

Isotopes Varieties of elements with same atomic number, same number of protons but different number of neutrons.

Allotropes Variety in physical form of chemical element.

Ac

Actinium

Actinium, named after *aktis*, Greek for ray,
as it is radioactive

Symbol: Ac	**Isotopes:** Most stable is
Atomic Number: 89	^{227}Ac (half-life 21.77 years)
Relative Atomic Mass: 227	**Others:** x 5:
Valency: Not known	^{224}Ac (hl 2.7 hours),
Element Type: Transitional,	^{225}Ac (hl 10.0 days),
rare-earth, actinide series	^{226}Ac (hl 1.224 days),
Group: Transitional **Period:** 7	^{228}Ac (hl 6.15 hours),
Relative Density: 10.07	^{229}Ac (hl 1.04 hours)
Melting or Fusing Point:	**Allotropes:** Not
1100°C (1900°F)	known
Boiling Point: 3200°C (5800°F)	

ACTINIUM is an extremely radioactive,
naturally occurring element that is
dangerous to deal with as it is 150 times
more radioactive than radium. It is
found within uranium ores, such as

*Pitchblende, an
important uranium ore,
also contains actinium.*

pitchblende, and can be isolated by using separation techniques
for rare-earth oxides. Actinium was discovered in 1899 by a
French chemist named André Debierne (1874–1949). The
element is the first of 15 in the actinide series of rare-earth
elements. It has very similar properties to lanthanum which is
its corresponding element in the lanthanide series. It is a silver-
grey substance in its pure state which decays into the elements
francium and helium. It has been put to practical use in the
generation of thermoelectric power and as a source of neutrons.

Aluminium $\qquad$ **Al**

Aluminium (aluminum in US), after alumina, which is
aluminium oxide, a major constituent of clays

Symbol: Al	**Relative Density:** 2.58
Atomic Number: 13	**Melting or Fusing Point:**
Relative Atomic Mass:	658°C (1220.38°F)
26.9815	**Boiling Point:** 1800°C (3272°F)
Valency: 3	**Isotopes:** Most common
Element Type: Metalloid	is ^{27}Al
Group: III **Period:** 3	**Allotropes:** Not known

ALUMINIUM is the most abundant metal element in the
crust of the Earth, occurring naturally in compounds in many
different rocks. The chief source of aluminium is an ore called
bauxite which contains high levels of aluminium oxide.
Aluminium is a silver-white metal in its pure state and
combines several useful properties. It is lightweight and
combines to form some hard-wearing and tough alloys with
relatively small amounts of
other elements such as
magnesium, manganese,
copper and silicon. Aluminium
was discovered in 1824 by the
Danish scientist Hans Oersted
(1777–1851) who is better
known for his work on
electromagnetism.

*Quality control checks on
aluminium rolls.*

Aluminium bars produced for storage.

Despite its abundance, aluminium is never found as a native metal and it remained an unused metal until Paul Heroult (1863–1914) and Charles Martin Hall (1863–1914), independently discovered, in the 1880s, that aluminium can be isolated from its ore using electrolysis. Their work led to the development of the Bayer process to extract aluminium, in which bauxite is mixed with caustic soda and heated. This produces crystals of pure aluminium oxide. These are dissolved in molten sodium aluminium fluoride. Electrolysis is then used to split the aluminium and oxygen.

This technique enabled the large-scale production of aluminium to take place, leading to it being used for a wide range of applications. Aluminium alloys have been employed in a range of technologies, from aircraft construction to kitchen utensils, to drink canisters and toothpaste tubes. As well as being lightweight and strong, aluminium alloys are also easy to machine, mould and cast into complex shapes. Aluminium is additionally non-magnetic and non-sparking, making it a desirable metal to use in devices where electrical and flammable materials are brought together.

Americium

Am

Americium, after America, the country of its discovery

Symbol: Am
Atomic Number: 95
Relative Atomic Mass: 243
Valency: 3, 4, 5, 7
Element Type: Transitional, rare-earth, actinide series
Group: Transitional **Period:** 7

Relative Density: 13.67
Melting or Fusing Point: 995°C (1821°F)
Boiling Point: Not known
Isotopes: Most stable is ^{243}Am (half-life 7650 years)
Allotropes: Not known

AMERICIUM has a beautiful silver-white lustre when freshly cut. It is not particularly reactive, tarnishing slowly with surface oxidation in dry, warm air. Being one of the actinide series, it is a radioactive rare-earth element and must be handled with care, for it emits alpha particles and gamma rays. It was discovered in 1944 by a team led by Glenn Seaborg (1912–95) at the University of California. Its creation was achieved with the capture of neutrons by plutonium isotopes in a particle accelerator. It is now known that it does also occur naturally in trace amounts in the uranium ore, pitchblende. Americium is used as a source of gamma rays and americium-241 is one of the weak radioactive sources which can be used used as a component in smoke alarms.

The American chemist Glenn Theodore Seaborg.

Sb

Antimony

Antimony, from Ancient Greek *anti-monos* meaning 'not alone' as it was thought not to exist in a pure state

Symbol: Sb from Latin *Stibium*	**Melting or Fusing Point:** 630.5°C (1166.9°F)
Atomic Number: 51	**Boiling Point:** 1750°C (3182°F)
Relative Atomic Mass: 121.75	**Isotopes:** Most common is ^{121}Sb
Valency: 3, 5	
Element Type: Metalloid	**Allotropes:** Two – bluish-white metallic form and amorphous grey form
Group: V **Period:** 5	
Relative Density: 6.62	

ANTIMONY, as its metalloid allotrope, has a bluish-white metallic lustre, but it is very brittle with a crystalline structure that readily flakes. Both the pure element and its compounds are toxic so a certain amount of caution must be observed when handling them. The most abundant source of antimony is a mineral ore called stibnite, which is a sulphide of the element. It is also found in other minerals such as ullminite, and is occasionally found in its native state, although it was not isolated in its pure form until the seventeenth century. At room temperature antimony is not reactive with air, but in a flame it readily burns with a brilliant light, producing copious quantities of white fumes.

Antimony is a poor conductor of heat and electricity, making it suitable as an ingredient in semiconductor materials for microelectronics. Its brittleness and hardness have long been recognised as desirable qualities in alloys of metals which are otherwise too malleable and soft for practical use. Lead alloys in particular have benefited greatly from the inclusion of antimony in their composition.

The element has been known in compound form since antiquity. One of antimony's most notable early uses was as an ingredient in Egyptian eyeliner, which was intended to serve as a deterrent for flies as well as beautifying the wearer. It is still used to this day for making pigments and has found other uses in medicines. It is employed in the manufacture of photosensitive substances for colour photography. Antimony is also part of the alloy used to make ball bearings.

Antimony was used in the eye makeup worn by the early Egyptians.

Ar
Argon

Argon, from the Greek word *argos* meaning
idle due to its inert nature

Symbol: Ar

Atomic Number: 18

Relative Atomic Mass: 39.948

Valency: 0

Element Type: Gas

Group: 0 **Period:** 3

Relative Density: 0.0017837

Melting or Fusing Point:
-189.4°C (-308.9°F)

Boiling Point: -185.9°C
(-302.6°F)

Isotopes: Three – ^{36}Ar,
^{38}Ar and ^{40}Ar being the
most common

Allotropes: Not known

The apparatus Ramsay used to prepare argon in quantity in 1894.

ARGON is one of the inert or noble gases. It was discovered in 1894 by Lord Rayleigh (1842–1919) and Sir William Ramsay (1852–1916). It makes up nearly 1% of the Earth's atmosphere, though it comprises three isotopes – ^{36}Ar, ^{38}Ar and ^{40}Ar – the last making up 99.6% of the total. As well as being inert, it is also colourless, tasteless and odourless. It is a monatomic element, since it exists as single atoms. The element is obtained in isolation by the fractional distillation of air. This involves the controlled heating of liquid air so that each of its gases is vaporised at its particular boiling point, in this case -185.9°C, and drawn off into a vessel.

The gas is useful in a number of ways because it is inert. It can be used for storing reactive elements as it prevents their oxidation. It is also used to fill electric light bulbs to prevent the electric filaments from oxidising as they glow. The gas will also carry an electric current and can therefore be used in fluorescent tubes and argon lasers. A steady stream of argon is used in the arc welding of aluminium to envelope the liquid metal thereby preventing it from oxidising. It also provides an inert environment in the production of semiconductors for microelectronics and the production of sheet glass.

Lord Rayleigh (above) and William Ramsay discovered argon in 1894.

As

Arsenic

Arsenic, from Greek *arsenikon* meaning 'yellow orpiment', a yellow ore of arsenic, Latin – *arsenicum*

Symbol: As
Atomic Number: 33
Relative Atomic Mass: 74.9216
Valency: 3, 5
Element Type: Metalloid
Group: V **Period:** 4
Relative Density: 5.73

Melting or Fusing Point: Sublimes at 613°C (1135°F)
Boiling Point: Sublimes at 613°C (1135°F)
Isotopes: Most common is ^{75}As
Allotropes: Three – black/grey arsenic, white arsenic and yellow (non-metallic) arsenic

Arsenic is very toxic, but in controlled doses it can be used in medicines.

ARSENIC, in its most usual metalloid form, is a steel-grey colour with a brittle, crystalline structure. The element is found in many metal ores and rarely as a native element. Ores include arsenolite, realgar, orpiment, arsenopyrite and loallingite. To isolate the element the ores are heated in the absence of air, causing the arsenic to sublime out of the ore as vapour which is subsequently condensed back into its solid form as a pure sample. It is produced commercially chiefly as a by-product of metallurgical processes, since it is often found in the same ores as metal elements such as iron, e.g. arsenopyrite.

In nature, arsenic is present in trace amounts in soil and seawater. It is also present, in minute quantities, in organisms, including humans. Arsenic and its compounds are well documented as poisons. An overdose of arsenic can cause death – it is a cumulative toxin which causes the body to exhibit increasingly violent symptoms as it builds up, ranging from vomiting to seizure. In controlled doses, however, arsenic can be used as a medicine because it will kill pathogens invading the body, despite the unpleasant side effects to the patient. The venereal disease syphilis was first treated in this way.

As well as being employed as a pesticide and herbicide, arsenic is used in certain alloys and solders. Being a metalloid it also possesses properties that make it suitable for making semiconductor materials for microelectronics. More obscure applications for arsenic include its use in pyrotechnics and as a laser material in the form of gallium arsenide.

Thomas Chatterton, an English poet, died after taking arsenic.

At

Astatine

Astatine, from Greek *astatos* meaning unstable

Symbol: At	**Melting or Fusing Point:**
Atomic Number: 85	302°C (575.6°F)
Relative Atomic Mass:	**Boiling Point:** 377°C
210/211	(710.6°F)
Valency: 1, 3, 5, 7	**Isotopes:** Most stable is
Element Type: Non-metal	^{210}At (half-life 8.3 hours)
Group: VII	some 20 in total,
Period: 6	all radioactive
Relative Density: Not known	**Allotropes:** Not known

ASTATINE is a rare element in nature. It occurs as the result of radioactive decay but has a short half-life so that it disappears almost as quickly as it occurs. It can, however, be artificially created by bombarding an isotope of the element bismuth with alpha particles. The astatine isotope ^{211}At can be used as a trace element in medicine as it collects in the thyroid gland and can be detected by X-rays. It has a half-life of just over eight hours which means that, although radioactive, it decays into harmless substances before it has been in the body for too long. The element was discovered in 1940 by a team led by Dale Corson at the University of California at Berkeley.

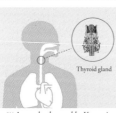

Thyroid gland

^{211}At can be detected by X-rays in the thyroid gland.

Barium

Ba

Barium, from Greek *barys* meaning heavy

Symbol: Ba	**Melting or Fusing Point:**
Atomic Number: 56	725°C (1337°F)
Relative Atomic Mass: 137.34	**Boiling Point:** 1640°C
Valency: 2	(2984°F)
Element Type: Metal	**Isotopes:** Most common
Group: II **Period:** 6	is ^{138}Ba
Relative Density: 3.51	**Allotropes:** Not known

BARIUM was discovered in 1808 by Sir Humphry Davy (1778–1829). It is one of the alkaline-earth metals and is most commonly found in the mineral ore barytes – also known as heavy spar – which is barium sulphate, or found in association with ores for other metals, such as lead, silver and zinc. Barium carbonate is another source, in the form of witherite.

Barium sulphate is opaque to X-rays, making it a useful medium for medical assessment of the alimentary canal. The barium sulphate is taken in suspension with a viscous liquid as a 'barium meal'. It then follows the course of the gut from the mouth through the stomach, small and large intestine to the anus.

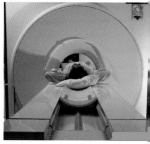

Barium sulphate is used in medical assessments of the alimentary canal.

When an X-ray is taken the barium sulphate reveals any abnormality due to the shape it assumes.

In its pure state barium is a soft, silver-white, lead-like metal. It is also used in alloys and vitreous pigments and in the ingredients of safety matches. In combination with strontium it is used for creating the emissive surface in cathode ray tubes.

Some rodent poisons and drying agents also contain barium. The alkaline-earth metals are all highly reactive soft metals. All tarnish rapidly with exposure to air, and barium typically reacts with water to form its hydroxide, which is a base that can be used for neutralising acids by producing a salt and water. The alkaline-earth metals are only ever bivalent (having a valency of two) and are only found in nature as compounds.

Sir Humphry Davy discovered barium in 1808.

Berkelium

Bk

Berkelium, after the University of California at Berkeley, where it was first discovered

Symbol: Bk
Atomic Number: 97
Relative Atomic Mass: 247
Valency: 3, 4
Element Type: Transitional, rare-earth, actinide series
Group: Transitional **Period:** 7
Relative Density: 14
(Calculated, not measured)

Melting or Fusing Point: 986°C (1807°F)
Boiling Point: Not known
Isotopes: Most stable is ^{247}Bk (half-life 1400 years), eight others are known
Allotropes: Not known

The American chemist, Glenn Theodore Seaborg.

BERKELIUM is one of the relatively recently discovered elements in the actinide series of radioactive rare-earth elements. It has only been created artificially in a laboratory environment. It is a silver-grey metallic element, discovered in December 1949 by the Berkeley team, led by Glenn Seaborg and Albert Ghiorso, at the University of California. It was created by bombarding americium with alpha particles. In 1962 the first visible quantity was produced – still only visble through a high-powered microscope as it weighed just 3 billionths of a gram. Berkelium has no uses as yet, though it is known to have a tendency to collect in skeletal systems, so it may eventually find a use in medical or scientific research.

Be
Beryllium

Beryllium, from Greek *beryllos* meaning beryl,
a mineral source of beryllium

Symbol: Be	**Melting or Fusing Point:** 1285°C (2345°F)
Atomic Number: 4	
Relative Atomic Mass: 9.0122	**Boiling Point:** 2469°C (4476°F)
Valency: 2	
Element Type: Metal	**Isotopes:** Most common is ^{9}Be
Group: II **Period:** 2	
Relative Density: 1.85	**Allotropes:** Not known

BERYLLIUM is a very
lightweight, silver-white,
alkaline-earth metal. It
was discovered in 1797
by French scientist Louis
Vauquelin (1763–1829)
as beryllium oxide, although
it was not isolated as a pure
element until 1828, by
Friedrich Wöhler and A. A.
B. Bussy, independently of
one another. It is the
principle ingredient in all
forms of beryl gemstones,

*Beryllium oxide ceramic is
used as a neutron regulator
in nuclear reactors.*

Analysis showed 'old' stars from the Milky Way contained beryllium.

such as emerald, beryl, aquamarine and morganite, which are its ores. Its extraction from these ores is a complex business with several methods used depending on the compound structure. Beryllium is one of just two of the six alkaline-earth metals that does not react with cold water to form a hydroxide; the other is magnesium. It also resists oxidation in air at room temperature, though it will form a thin oxide patina which betrays its presence by beryllium's ability to scratch glass.

Beryllium is used to make lightweight yet rigid alloys with copper and nickel for precision components in high-performance aircraft, missiles and so on. When beryllium is alloyed with steel the product is an exceptionally resilient metal, used for heavy-duty springs.

Beryllium is also used in X-ray machines and as a neutron regulator in nuclear reactors, where it is seen in the form of a beryllium oxide ceramic which can cope with extremely high temperatures. In 1992 scientific analysis of six 'old' stars in the Milky Way produced unexpected reults showing that they each contained high levels of beryllium.

Bi

Bismuth

Bismuth, from New Latin *bisemutum*,
from German *Wismut*, of unknown origin

Symbol: Bi	**Relative Density:** 9.75
Atomic Number: 83	**Melting or Fusing Point:**
Relative Atomic Mass:	271.3°C (520.3°F)
208.9806	**Boiling Point:** 1560°C (2840°F)
Valency: 3, 5	**Isotopes:** Most common
Element Type: Metal	is ^{209}Bi
Group: V **Period:** 6	**Allotropes:** Not known

BISMUTH is a crystalline and brittle metal. It is silver-white
with a faint hint of pink in colour. It is the most diamagnetic
of the metal elements, meaning that it is repelled from regions
of high magnetic field. Bismuth is second only to mercury in
its lack of thermal conductivity and has a high resistance to
electricity. In fact bismuth's resistance to conducting electricity
increases when it is placed in a magnetic field. This is known as
the Hall Effect, named after Edwin Hall (1855–1938).

Bismuth is one of the elements that has been known since
ancient times, though going by early written accounts it seems
previously to have been confused with both tin and lead. Its
compounds were described by Valentine in 1450, but it was
the Frenchman, Claude Geoffroy the Younger, who isolated
bismuth and showed the difference between the metals in 1753.

The chief ores from which bismuth is obtained are bismite
and bismuthinite. The element is used for making very low
melting point alloys that act as irreversible thermal switches for

sprinkler systems. Bismuth expands when it solidifies or freezes making it a useful ingredient in alloys for casting very detailed items such as jewellery components. It is also used in insoluble compounds for treating ailments such as gastric ulcers and skin injuries. With the highest thermoelectric effect known, bismuth is employed as an ingredient for thermocouples, used for measuring temperatures. It also finds a use in catalysing the chemical reactions for producing acrylic fibres in the chemical textile industry.

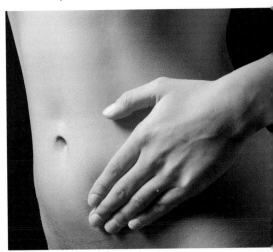

Bismuth is used in the treatment of gastric ulcers and skin injuries.

Bh

Bohrium

Bohrium, after Danish physicist Niels Bohr (1885–1962)

Symbol: Bh	**Group:** Transitional **Period:** 7
Atomic Number: 107	**Relative Density:** Not known
Relative Atomic Mass: 264	**Melting or Fusing Point:**
Valency: Not known	Not known
Element Type: Transitional,	**Boiling Point:** Not known
radioactive rare-earth,	**Isotopes:** Not known
actinide series	**Allotropes:** Not known

BOHRIUM is one of the highly radioactive rare-earth elements that does not exist in nature and has only been created artificially in a laboratory environment. Following its discovery it was initially called unnilseptium by the International Union of Pure and Applied Chemistry to satisfy arguments between scientists from the West and Russia (formerly USSR). The Russians claimed to have discovered it first in 1976 but this was not universally accepted until a German team substantiated their work in 1981. Bohrium has never been isolated as more than a few atoms and has there-fore never been visually observed. It also decays extremely rapidly, having a half-life of just 102 milliseconds or 102 thousandths of a second. It has no known uses as yet.

Bohrium was named after Niels Bohr.

Boron

B

Boron, from bor(ax), its ore, and (carb)on,
to which it is adjacent in the periodic table

Symbol: B
Atomic Number: 5
Relative Atomic Mass: 10.81
Valency: 3
Element Type: Metalloid
Group: III **Period:** 2
Relative Density:
    2.34 (as crystals),
    2.37 (amorphous type)

Melting or Fusing Point:
    2079°C (3774°F)
Boiling Point: Sublimes at
    2550°C (4622°F)
Isotopes: Most common
    is ^{11}B, also ^{10}B is
    most stable
Allotropes: Two – crystalline
    and amorphous

BORON displays properties that fall between the metals and
non-metals, which is why it is considered a metalloid. It can
exist in two allotropes or physical forms. In its amorphous form

Boron absorbs neutrons in nuclear reactors and particle counters.

Sir Humphry Davy was one of the first scientists to isolate boron.

boron is an impure brown-coloured powder, but its pure form is a black or dark-grey crystalline structure with a silvery sheen. It can be isolated from various minerals, though its most abundant ores are kernite and borax.

The compounds of boron have been known since ancient times but it was not isolated and identified as an element until 1808, and then by three scientists. They were French chemists Joseph-Louis Gay Lussac (1778–1850) and Louis Jacques Thénard (1777–1857) who worked together, and English scientist Sir Humphry Davy who made his discovery independently. They reacted boric acid with potassium to obtain the pure boron.

Being a metalloid, boron has suitable properties for semiconductor materials in microelectronics. It is also used for neutron absorption in nuclear reactors and particle counters. Boric or orthoboric acid is a white, soluble, crystalline substance containing boron, which is used as a mild antiseptic in medicinal ointments. It is also used in the manufacture of heat-resistant glass and vitreous porcelain enamels as well as fire-resistant materials. Borax is a boron-containing, white, fusible mineral which finds uses as a softener in washing powders, as a flux for soldering and as an ingredient of fertilisers. Borides are compounds of boron and metals. They are extremely tough and heat resistant, making very good abrasives and refractories.

Bromine

Br

Bromine, from Greek word *bromos*
meaning stench – from its odour

Symbol: Br	**Relative Density:** 3.12
Atomic Number: 35	**Melting or Fusing Point:**
Relative Atomic Mass: 79.904	-7.2°C (19.04°F)
Valency: 1, 3, 5, 7	**Boiling Point:** 58.8°C (137.8°F)
Element Type: Liquid,	**Isotopes:** Most common
non-metal	is ^{79}Br
Group: VII **Period:** 4	**Allotropes:** Not known

BROMINE is the only non-metal element that is a liquid at room temperature. In its liquid state it is a dark, reddish-brown colour and it readily gives off toxic fumes of a similar colour with an unpleasant smell. As a solid, when frozen, bromine takes on a metallic sheen. Bromine must be handled very carefully because its fumes cause irritation to the eyes, nose and throat. Combined with water, a bleaching agent is produced by these vapours. The liquid itself will create nasty sores if it comes into contact with skin. Being such a dangerous health hazard, bromine must always be handled following a strict safety code.

Antoine Balard was one of two scientists who discovered bromine.

The most common source of bromine is seawater, where it exists in the salt sodium bromide, although sodium chloride – or common salt – is present in far greater quantities.

Being less reactive than chlorine, the bromine can be released from its compound by treating the seawater with chlorine gas. Bromine was discovered in 1826 by the Frenchman Antoine Balard (1802–76) and the German Carl Löwig – although the announcement of the latter's discovery was delayed because he had some exams to take, thus Balard's report took precedence.

Bromine can form organic and inorganic compounds, both of which have various uses. A dye colour, known as Tyrian purple, was originally obtained from the shell of a mollusc. It was eventually found to be an organobromide compound produced by the animal, a discovery which enabled it to be manufactured artificially.

Bromine compounds are very easily changed by light which is why they can be used in photographic films.

Cadmium

Cd

Cadmium, derived from the Latin and Greek words *cadmia* and *kadmeia*, both meaning calamine which is actually zinc carbonate. Cadmium was first found in calamine

Symbol: Cd	**Melting or Fusing Point:**
Atomic Number: 48	320.9° (609.6°F)
Relative Atomic Mass: 112.4	**Boiling Point:** 765°C
Valency: 2	(1409°F)
Element Type: Transitional	**Isotopes:** Most common
Group: Transitional **Period:** 5	is ^{114}Cd
Relative Density: 8.65	**Allotropes:** Not known

CADMIUM is a malleable transitional element, silver-white with a bluish tinge. It is similar to zinc in its properties, though it is soft enough to cut with a knife, upon which it emits a noise described as a 'scream'. The element is highly poisonous, both pure and in compound, so should be handled with appropriate care. It is also an environmental hazard, especially in water. Shellfish can accumulate dangerously high

Shellfish accumulate concentrations of cadmium from filtering water for food.

concentrations of cadmium as they filter the water for food.

Cadmium was first isolated and discovered in 1817 by the German chemist Friedrich Strohmeyer (1776–1835). He managed to separate small quantities of cadmium from zinc carbonate or calamine, prompted by an observation that colour changes occurred upon heating it that indicated the presence of another substance. Although usually extracted from zinc and lead ores, cadmium is also found in the mineral greenockite which is a sulphide.

The element is used as an ingredient in some specialist alloys and solders, providing low friction and high fatigue-resistance properties. It is also used in the electroplating of reactive metals such as iron. In combination with nickel it is used to produce nickel–cadmium batteries. Cadmium yellow is another name for cadmium sulphide – an insoluble compound with a deep yellow colour, used as a pigment in paints. Cadmium can also be found in the phosphors applied to television tubes, as control rods and shields in nuclear reactors and as a stabilising medium in the manufacture of some plastics.

Cadmium, combined with nickel, is used to make batteries.

Caesium

Cs

Caesium (Cesium in US), from the Latin *caesius*
meaning 'heavenly blue'

Symbol: Cs	**Relative Density:** 1.87
Atomic Number: 55	**Melting or Fusing Point:**
Relative Atomic Mass:	28.4°C (83.1°F)
132.9055	**Boiling Point:** 678°C (1252°F)
Valency: 1	**Isotopes:** Most common
Element Type: Metal	is ^{133}Cs, also ^{137}Cs
Group: I **Period:** 6	**Allotropes:** Not known

CAESIUM was given its name because it characteristically
displays two bright lines in the blue end of its spectrum whilst
under spectrum analysis. It is a silver-white metal and is very
soft and ductile. Although the element mercury is often
thought of as the only liquid metal, caesium will melt in the
hand, having a melting point only a few degrees above room
temperature, as does the element gallium. This metal was

discovered in 1860 using spectrum
analysis by Gustav Kirchhoff (1824–87)
and Robert Bunsen (1811–99), both
from Germany. It is used in the
manufacture of photoelectric cells, and
the isotope ^{137}Cs is employed in the
treatment of cancers. Caesium is
highly reactive with water, being a
typical alkali metal in this respect.

Robert Bunsen, a pioneer of chemical spectroscopy.

Ca

Calcium

Calcium, from Latin word *calx* or *calcis* meaning lime, which is actually calcium carbonate, calcium hydroxide, calcium oxide and calcium sulphate

Symbol: Ca	**Melting or Fusing Point:**
Atomic Number: 20	839°C (1542°F)
Relative Atomic Mass: 40.08	**Boiling Point:** 1484°C
Valency: 2	(2703°F)
Element Type: Metal	**Isotopes:** Most common
Group: II **Period:** 4	is ^{40}Ca
Relative Density: 1.55	**Allotropes:** Not known

Some cements contain calcium combined with other materials.

CALCIUM is a common alkaline-earth metal, accounting for about 3% of the Earth's crust. It is a silver-white and fairly hard metal in its pure elemental form, but is associated with many whitish mineral compounds such as chalk, limestone and gypsum. Biologically it is very important for the maintenance of strong and healthy teeth, nails and bones, as well as playing a vital role in regulating the heartbeat. Calcium, as a metal, is rarely used for anything, but it is a highly reactive element readily combining with other elements to form a variety of compounds useful to both humans and nature.

Calcium was discovered and named in 1808 by Sir Humphry Davy in the same year that he discovered the elements barium, magnesium, strontium and boron. He used electrolysis to isolate the metal from lime.

Calcium has many uses. As early as AD 975 plaster of Paris was described as a useful material for setting broken bones. The plaster is dehydrated gypsum or calcium sulphate, which reacts with water to form a hard, rigid hydrous form. Portland cement also contains calcium in the form of chalk or lime baked with clay.

Calcium is never found free or native in nature because it is so reactive, especially with oxygen and water. A characteristic of calcium is that it produces a brick-red colour in its flame test. Calcium is the fifth most abundant of the Earth's elements and the third most abundant metal, after the elements aluminium and iron.

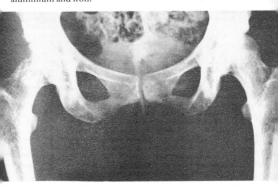

Calcium is essential for the maintenance of healthy teeth, nails and bones.

Cf

Californium

Californium, after the state where the University of
California, Berkeley is located

Symbol: Cf	**Melting or Fusing Point:** Not known
Atomic Number: 98	**Boiling Point:** Not known
Relative Atomic Mass: 251	**Isotopes:** Most stable is
Valency: Not known	^{251}Cf (half-life 800 years),
Element Type: Transitional, rare-earth, actinide series	also ^{252}Cf
Group: Transitional **Period:** 7	**Allotropes:** Not known
Relative Density: Not known	

CALIFORNIUM is one
of the highly radioactive
rare-earth elements from
the actinide series that
has only been artificially
produced in a laboratory.
Californium was made by
bombarding curium-242 with

*Californium
is used in the
detection of silver-
bearing minerals.*

helium ions. It was discovered in this way in
1950 by a team led by Glenn Seaborg and Albert Ghiorso. Only
tiny quantities have ever been created, so the appearance and
many properties of the element are unknown. Biologically it is an
extremely hazardous element as a microgram would emit 170
million neutrons per minute. Consequently californium-252
has been used as a source of neutrons and for fission fragments
in research experimentation. It has also been used in the
detection of gold, silver and oil-bearing minerals.

Carbon

C

Carbon, from Latin word *carbo* meaning charcoal,
which is high in carbon content

Symbol: C

Atomic Number: 6

Relative Atomic Mass: 12.011

Carbon: 2, 4

Element Type: Non-metal

Group: IV **Period:** 2

Relative Density: 1.9–2.3
graphite. 3.15–3.53
diamond

Melting or Fusing Point:
Sublimes at 3367°C
(6093°F). Melts 3550°C
(6422°F)

Boiling Point: 4200°C
(7592°F)

Isotopes: Most common is
^{12}C; also ^{14}C radioactive

Allotropes: Graphite (various
amorphous forms),
diamond and
buckminsterfullerene

*Coal contains many
carbon compounds.*

CARBON exists in every
organic molecule, since the
Earth is home to carbon-
based life forms. It is
possible that silicon-based
life forms exist on other
planets in the universe,
because it can form similarly
complex compounds. The vast array of organic compounds
are known as hydrocarbons, because the carbon bonds with
hydrogen and other non-metal elements. Carbon has three
allotropes. Diamond is the hardest substance known, measuring

ten on the Mohs Scale, while graphite, another carbon allotrope, is extremely soft. This is because in graphite the carbon atoms are arranged in sliding layers while in diamond they form a three-dimensional lattice structure. Graphite and diamond have been known since antiquity but a third allotrope, buckminsterfullerene, sometimes known as 'buckyballs', was discovered in 1996 by Harold Kroto and David Walton. Its atoms are arranged into spheres like the geodesic domes that American architect, Richard Buckminster Fuller, invented using hexagonal and pentagonal facets.

Carbon has many uses. Fossil fuels such as coal and petroleum oil contain many carbon compounds and amorphous forms of carbon. The carbon compounds in oil can be separated by a process called fractional distillation and are employed in all kinds of domestic and industrial ways. Diamonds are used as abrasives as well as gemstones. Carbon dating uses the rate of decay of the radioactive isotope carbon-14, which occurs naturally in living organisms, to date objects. Buckminsterfullerene spheres can be used to contain metal atoms, thereby creating compounds that behave as semiconductors.

The largest-ever colourless diamond to be auctioned.

Cerium

Ce

Cerium, after the asteroid Ceres discovered
two years prior to the element in 1801

Symbol: Ce	**Relative Density:** 6.77
Atomic Number: 58	**Melting or Fusing Point:**
Relative Atomic Mass: 140.12	798°C (1468°F)
Valency: 3, 4	**Boiling Point:** 3257°C
Element Type: Transitional,	(5895°F)
rare-earth, lanthanide	**Isotopes:** Most common
series	is ^{140}Ce
Group: Transitional **Period:** 6	**Allotropes:** Not known

CERIUM is the most abundant of the lanthanide series of rare-earth elements. It is a ductile iron-grey element with a metallic lustre. As a reactive rare-earth element it comes second only to the element europium, decomposing rapidly when immersed in hot water. It will also ignite under friction, for example when scraped with a knife. Its chief source is the ore mineral monazite.
Cerium was discovered coincidentally in
1803 by scientists in Germany and
Sweden. They were Jöns Berzelius
(1766–1848) and Wilhelm von Hisinger
(1766–1852) of Sweden, and Martin
Klaproth (1743–1817) of Germany.
Cerium has found various uses, such as in
lighter flint alloys and the cores of carbon
electrodes in arc lamps. It is also used in
nuclear fuels and in glass production.

Cerium is used in the production of glass.

Cl

Chlorine

Chlorine, from Greek *chloros* describing 'pale green'

Symbol: Cl	**Melting or Fusing Point:** -101°C (-149.8°F)
Atomic Number: 17	
Relative Atomic Mass: 35.453	**Boiling Point:** -34.6°C (-30.28°F)
Valency: 1, 3, 5, 7	
Element Type: Gas	**Isotopes:** Most common is ^{35}Cl
Group: VII **Period:** 3	
Relative Density: Not known	**Allotropes:** Single

CHLORINE is a gaseous element at room temperature. It is a noxious, toxic gas with a yellowish-green colour and a very pungent odour. It does not occur in its elemental form in nature, being a chemically reactive gas which will combine readily with most metals to form salt compounds. The most familiar is common salt or sodium chloride, which is used as the main source for isolating chlorine.

Chlorination disinfects and purifies water.

Chlorine is recovered from seawater or brine – water with sodium chloride dissolved in it – by electrolysis. The element was first discovered in 1774 by a Swedish scientist named Carl William Scheele (1742–86) and given its common name by Sir Humphry Davy in 1810.

One of its more familiar uses is as a purifier and disinfectant of water for drinking and bathing, by the process of chlorination. It is also used widely as a bleaching agent for wood pulp in the production of paper and as a general domestic germicidal cleanser. Due to its poisonous properties, chlorine gas was employed as a chemical weapon on the battlefields during the First World War. As it is heavier than air it found its way into dugouts and trenches where it attacked the mucous membranes inside soldiers' lungs and burned their skin, leading to many deaths. Chlorine is also used in the manufacture of chloroform, or trichloromethane, which used to be a major anaesthetic, and is still used in cough remedies and as a chemical solvent. Various plastics and pesticides also use chlorine compounds.

Some compounds of the toxic, noxious gas, chlorine, are effective germicidal bleaching agents.

Cr **Chromium**

Chromium, from Greek for colour – *chroma*

Symbol: Cr	**Melting or Fusing Point:**
Atomic Number: 24	1890°C (3434°F)
Relative Atomic Mass: 51.996	**Boiling Point:** 2672°C
Valency: 2, 3, 6	(4842°F)
Element Type: Transitional	**Isotopes:** Most common
Group: Transitional **Period:** 4	is ^{52}Cr
Relative Density: 7.19	**Allotropes:** Not known

CHROMIUM is a hard, metallic, transitional element. It is a dull, steel-grey but has a bright, beautiful 'chrome' lustre when polished. For this reason it is very popular as an electroplated coating for iron and steel objects. It was given its name because chromium compounds produce an array of colours. Crocoite, for example, is a highly valued, red oil-paint pigment containing chromium, and the green of emerald gemstones is due to chromium, while lead chromate is yellow. The main ore of chromium is called chromite. This was discovered by a German chemist, B. M. Tassaert, though the element itself had been

discovered some two years previously in 1797 by Frenchman, Louis Vauquelin (1763–1829). Chromium is an important component of stainless steel.

Molten iron flows from a blast furnace. Chromium is added to iron in the making of stainless steel.

Cobalt Co

Cobalt, from German *kobald* which is a name for
an evil, mischievous spirit or goblin

Symbol: Co
Atomic Number: 27
Relative Atomic Mass:
58.9332
Valency: 2, 3
Element Type: Transitional
Group: Transitional **Period:** 4
Relative Density: 8.9

Melting or Fusing Point:
1495°C (2723°F)
Boiling Point: 2870°C (5198°F)
Isotopes: Most common is
^{59}Co, also cobalt-60 (half-
life 5.26 years)
Allotropes: Not known

COBALT is a metallic, transitional
element which is hard and brittle in
its pure form. It can be identified by
its magnetic property, just like iron.
It has a lustrous, greyish surface. The
primary cobalt ores are cobaltite and
smaltite, though cobalt does occur
rarely as a free or native element.
Cobalt-rich minerals were known to
the Ancient Egyptians, Sumerians
and Babylonians who used them for
producing blue-coloured glass.
'Cobalt blue' is the same compound
– a cobalt salt – still used as a
vitreous pigment and in artists'
paints. A Swedish chemist, Georg
Brandt (1694–1768) discovered

*Cobalt, as part of vitamin
B12, is essential for a
healthy human body.*

Cobalt can be used to make blue glass.

cobalt in 1737 by analysing blue glass and distinguishing it from the element bismuth which is quite often found in association with cobalt.

Vitamin B12 includes cobalt as one of its constituents, making it essential to human health. Another way in which cobalt benefits health is in the form of cobalt-60. This is an artificially produced radioactive substance used in radiotherapy and for conducting tracer studies, because it produces gamma radiation. Cobalt is also used as a component of hard, high-temperature tool steels, and in alloys for casting into magnets, such as Alnico. It can also be used for electroplating as it is resistant to oxidation as well as having a hard and attractive finish. Analysis of some metallic meteorites has shown them to contain cobalt. Erythrite, often described as cobalt bloom, is a peach-red mineral occasionally found above ground, as it is the result of weathering of cobalt ores.

Copper

Cu

Copper, from *cuprum* which is the Latin
name for the island of Cyprus

Symbol: Cu. Abbreviation for the Latin *cuprum*	**Relative Density:** 8.96
Atomic Number: 29	**Melting or Fusing Point:** 1083°C (1981°F)
Relative Atomic Mass: 63.546	**Boiling Point:** 2567°C (4653°F)
Valency: 1, 2	**Isotopes:** Most common is ^{63}Cu
Element Type: Transitional	
Group: Transitional **Period:** 4	**Allotropes:** Single

COPPER is one of the elements known to man since antiquity. It occurs in its native state as nuggets, though greater quantities exist in ores, such as cuprite and chalcopyrite. Copper is a malleable transitional element, although it is popularly thought of as a metal. Freshly cut, it has a bright red-pink lustre, but its surface tarnishes rapidly to a dull red-brown colour as it oxidises. Copper used for roofing and statues turns a greenish-blue colour because it reacts with acid rain, producing a patina of copper sulphate crystals (blue vitriol).

A piece of copper ore. Once exposed to the air copper tarnishes through oxidation.

Copper was the first 'metal' to be extensively used by people for making tools and weapons. When it was discovered that copper forms a harder and more durable alloy with tin, the Copper Age gave way to the Bronze Age (*c.* 2000–500 BC in Britain), which lasted until the advent of the Iron Age.

Copper is a very good conductor of heat and electricity, as well as being malleable and corrosion resistant, explaining why it is still used extensively, especially for central heating and wiring. Brass, an alloy of copper and zinc, also has many applications. The alloy selected for a given purpose will depend on the properties required – in terms of hardness, malleability, strength or appearance, for example. Copper and its alloys have been used in the manufacture of coins and other tokens for thousands of years world-wide. Vast quantities of copper are now also used for copper-plating iron and steel components because copper is ideal as an electrical primer onto which other, more attractive, finishes can be electroplated.

A large single crystal of copper sulphate.

Curium

Cm

Curium, named after Pierre (1859–1906)
and Marie Curie (1867–1934)

Symbol: Cm
Atomic Number: 96
Relative Atomic Mass: 247
Valency: 3
Element Type: Transitional,
rare-earth, actinide series
Group: Transitional **Period:** 7
Relative Density: 13.51
(calculated)

Melting or Fusing Point:
1340°C (2444°F)
Boiling Point: Not known
Isotopes: 14 known, most
stable is ^{247}Cm (half-life
1.6×10^7 years)
Allotropes: Not known

Pierre and Marie Curie.

CURIUM is a member of the
actinide series of rare-earth
elements that have only been
created artificially. This was
achieved in 1944 by the team
led by Glenn Seaborg and Albert Ghiorso at the University
of California, Berkeley. The method employed was to bombard
a plutonium isotope with alpha particles. At first only curium
hydroxide, a yellowish compound, could be created, but 1951
saw the isolation of curium in its elemental form. Curium is
silver in appearance and highly dangerous due to its
radioactivity. Its most stable isotope – ^{247}Cm – has a half-life of
16 million years. The element can accumulate in the bones of
the body where it affects the red-cell forming mechanism,
destroying it by toxic radiation. It may occur naturally in tiny
quantities in uranium ores.

Db

Dubnium

Dubnium, after the Joint Nuclear Institute
of Dubna in Russia

Symbol: Db	**Group:** Transitional **Period:** 7
Atomic Number: 105	**Relative Density:** Not known
Relative Atomic Mass: 261	**Melting or Fusing Point:** Not known
Valency: Not known	**Boiling Point:** Not known
Element Type: Transitional, rare-earth, actinide series	**Isotopes:** Not known
	Allotropes: Not known

DUBNIUM was initially named unnilpentium (Unp) by the
International Union of Pure and Applied Chemistry in 1980,

*Dubnium was
discovered by the
Russians in 1967.*

due to arguments between scientists from
the US and the USSR who each wanted to
call it different names, believing they had
discovered it first. Discovered in 1967, it
was eventually agreed that the Russians
had got there before the Americans.
Interestingly, the two teams created
dubnium in different ways. The Russian
team, led by Georgii Flerov, bombarded
americium ions with neon ions, whilst the
Americans, led by Albert Ghiorso,
collided californium ions with nitrogen
ions. Dubnium has never been created in
a sufficient quantity to know anything of
its physical appearance. Dubnium does
not have any known uses.

Dysprosium

Dy

Dysprosium, from Greek *dysproitos*
meaning 'hard to find or obtain'

Symbol: Dy	**Relative Density:** 8.54
Atomic Number: 66	**Melting or Fusing Point:**
Relative Atomic Mass: 162.5	1409°C (2568°F)
Valency: 3	**Boiling Point:** 2335°C
Element Type: Transitional,	(4235°F)
rare-earth, lanthanide	**Isotopes:** Most common
series	is ^{164}Dy
Group: Transitional **Period:** 6	**Allotropes:** Not known

DYSPROSIUM was discovered as an impurity in erbium oxide
in 1886 by French chemist, Paul Lecoq de Boisbaudran
(1838–1912). It was not actually isolated in elemental form
until the 1950s with the development of techniques called ion-
exchange and metallographic reduction,
hence the choice of name. Dysprosium is a
metallic, transitional element with a silvery-
white lustre. It is quite stable in air at room
temperature but will dissolve in water and is
soft enough to be sliced with a knife. The
ores containing dysprosium include monazite
and bastnaesite. Dysprosium has various
uses, being found in lasers, compact discs
and the control systems of nuclear reactors as
a neutron absorber. It is also used in some
specialist stainless steels that require the
specific properties it has to offer.

*Dysprosium
is used in the
manufacture of
lasers.*

Es Einsteinium

Einsteinium, after Albert Einstein (1879–1955)

Symbol: Es
Atomic Number: 99
Relative Atomic Mass: 254
Valency: 2, 3
Element Type: Transitional, rare-earth, actinide series
Group: Transitional **Period:** 7

Relative Density: Not known
Melting or Fusing Point: Not known
Boiling Point: Not known
Isotopes: Most stable is ^{254}Es (half-life 276 days), also ^{253}Es (half-life 20 days)
Allotropes: Not known

Einstein's name was given to this element.

EINSTEINIUM is one of the transuranic elements, meaning that it has an atomic number greater than uranium's which is 92. It is a radioactive, rare-earth element from the actinide series and was discovered in 1952, three years before the death of Einstein, when it was named after him. The element was originally detected as a decay product of uranium in the fallout following the detonation of the first large hydrogen – or thermonuclear – bomb, as isotope ^{253}Es which has a half-life of 20 days. Scientists at Argonne, Los Alamos and at the University of California, Berkeley, contributed to its discovery by creating isotope ^{254}Es. Einsteinium has not been produced in sufficient amounts to know anything of its physical appearance or its possible uses.

Erbium

Er

Erbium, derived from 'erb' in Ytterby, a Swedish town.
Not to be confused with Ytterbium and Terbium,
also named after Ytterby

Symbol: Er	**Relative Density:** 9.045
Atomic Number: 68	**Melting or Fusing Point:**
Relative Atomic Mass: 167.26	1522°C (2772°F)
Valency: 3	**Boiling Point:** 2863°C (5185°F)
Element Type: Transitional, rare-earth, lanthanide series	**Isotopes:** Most common is ^{166}Er, six natural known, 12 radioactive
Group: Transitional **Period:** 6	**Allotropes:** Not known

ERBIUM is a rare-earth element of the lanthanide series.
It is a shiny silver-white colour in its elemental form, though
it often contains trace amounts of impurities that affect its
properties and make it look greyish. As a pure sample it is soft
and malleable. For a rare-earth element it is fairly stable and
does not oxidise as readily as others. It occurs in six natural
isotopes, all of which can be isolated from its ore minerals,
such as monazite and bastnaesite. There are also 12 known
radioactive isotopes.

The 15 lanthanide elements are all very similar to one
another, which is why they are located together in the same
series in the periodic table. In fact their properties alter only
slightly as their atomic numbers increase from 57 to 71. Only
promethium, at 61, is naturally radioactive.

Erbium was discovered in 1843 by Swedish chemist, Carl
Mosander (1797–1858), along with the element terbium and

what he called 'didymium', which was later shown to be a combination of the elements neodymium and praseodymium. Erbium has various applications. It is used in some special alloys to make other elements, such as vanadium, less hard and more workable, while its oxide is used as a pink pigment in glass and vitreous enamels. In 1987 erbium was used in transmission amplifiers for pulses of data sent along fibre-optic cables. It works through erbium ions, trapped within the glass filament, becoming excited by infrared light and emitting pulses of energy, thereby amplifying the conveyed light signals.

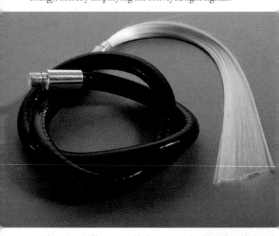

Erbium ions in fibre-optic cables become stimulated by infrared light and emit pulses of energy.

Europium

Eu

Europium, named after Europe

Symbol: Eu	**Relative Density:** 5.25
Atomic Number: 63	**Melting or Fusing Point:** 822°C (1512°F)
Relative Atomic Mass: 151.96	
Valency: 2, 3	**Boiling Point:** 1597°C (2907°F)
Element Type: Transitional, rare-earth, lanthanide series	**Isotopes:** Most common is ^{153}Eu
Group: Transitional **Period:** 6	**Allotropes:** Not known

EUROPIUM was discovered between 1896 and 1901 and the scientist who took the credit was Eugene Demarcay (1852–1903), though europium oxide had been identified in 1889 by William Crookes (1832–1919). In fact Demarcay had still only succeeded in extracting an impure sample of europium from material which included a high percentage of the element samarium. Pure samples of europium were only achieved in the late twentieth century. It is a silvery-white colour and will ignite in air when it reaches between 150–180°C (302–356°F). The most reactive of its series, europium oxidises readily in air. It finds uses in various alloys and in the coating of colour television tubes. Europium isotopes are used as neutron absorbers in nuclear reactors.

Europium is used to coat colour television tubes.

Fm Fermium

Fermium, named after physicist Enrico Fermi (1901–54)

Symbol: Fm	**Relative Density:** Not known
Atomic Number: 100	**Melting or Fusing Point:** Not known
Relative Atomic Mass: 257	
Valency: 2, 3	**Boiling Point:** Not known
Element Type: Transitional, rare-earth, actinide series	**Isotopes:** Most stable is ^{257}Fm (half-life 80 days), ten known
Group: Transitional	
Period: 7	**Allotropes:** Not known

FERMIUM, like einsteinium, was first identified, and therefore discovered, in 1952 as a decay product of uranium in the fallout of the first large hydrogen – or thermonuclear – bomb detonation. As it has only ever been produced in trace amounts, this element has no known uses. For the same reason, nothing is known of its appearance and little about its properties. The team led by Glenn Seaborg and Albert Ghiorso at the University of California, Berkeley, was behind the confirmation of its discovery. Enrico Fermi, the scientist after whom the element was named, was an Italian-born US physicist who pioneered work in nuclear physics. He built the first nuclear reactor in 1942, having achieved the first self-sustaining uranium chain reaction and worked on the development of the atomic bomb.

Fermium was identified in the fallout of a hydrogen bomb.

Fluorine

F

Fluorine, after Latin for 'a flowing'

Symbol: F	**Period:** 2
Atomic Number: 9	**Relative Density:** -223
Relative Atomic Mass: 18.9984	**Melting or Fusing Point:** -219.6°C (-363.3°F)
Valency: 1	**Boiling Point:** -188.1°C (-306.6°F)
Element Type: Gas, non-metal	**Isotopes:** Single – ^{19}F
Group: VII	**Allotropes:** Single

FLUORINE is a pale yellow gaseous element with a pungent odour. It is a member of the halogen group and is a toxic substance in elemental form. It was discovered in 1771 by Swedish chemist Carl William Scheele, but was not isolated until 1886, by French chemist Ferdinand Moissan (1852–1907). Fluorine is a highly reactive gas which will form compounds with almost all other elements and attack many existing compounds. It occurs in mineral ores such as fluorite and cryolite, from which it is easily obtained by electrolysis since it is the most electronegative of the elements.

Fluorides are fluorine salts. They are added to public

Aerosols used to contain harmful CFCs. Sprays containing these flourine-based gases have now been banned.

water supplies and toothpastes to help prevent tooth decay. Fluoridation works because fluorine compounds are formed in the outer layers of teeth that are resistant to the acids generated by bacteria in the mouth.

Fluorite, or fluospar, is the glassy, semi-precious mineral calcium fluoride, which comes in a variety of colours, including blue, purple, green and yellow. As well as its decorative uses, calcium fluoride is employed as a flux – a substance mixed with a metal oxide to assist in fusion – in steel production and in ceramics. Fluorine compounds are used in some plastics, such as polytetrafluoroethylene (PTFE), otherwise known as Teflon, which is a non-stick and low-friction material. The liquids used in refrigerators for heat exchange also often contain fluorine. They are known as CFCs or chlorofluorocarbons. These are harmful to the environment because they contribute to the hole in the ozone layer which protects the Earth from harmful ultraviolet light rays. The complete phasing-out of harmful CFCs is now a worldwide objective but a safe substitute needs to be developed before their use can be universally banned.

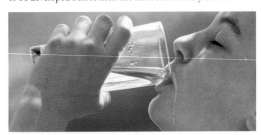

Fluorides are added to water supplies to help teeth resist decay.

Francium

Fr

Francium, named after France

Symbol: Fr
Atomic Number: 87
Relative Atomic Mass: 223
Valency: 1
Element Type: Metal, alkali
Group: I **Period:** 7
Relative: Not known

Melting or Fusing Point: Not known
Boiling Point: Not known
Isotopes: Most stable is ^{223}Fr, 21 identified
Allotropes: Not known

FRANCIUM belongs to the alkali metals group and is silvery-white in appearance. It occurs in nature as a decay product of actinium, but in very minute quantities. It was discovered in 1939 by French chemist, Marguérite Perey (1909–75), who chose to honour her country with her choice of name. The longest lived isotope of francium – ^{223}Fr – has a half-life of a mere 21 minutes, making it difficult to study before it decays. The alkali metals all have very low densities and are soft, with low melting points. They are reactive elements and are therefore only found as compounds in nature, though francium only exists in passing as a component element in a radioactive decay chain: actinium, francium, astatine.

Francium was discovered by Marguérite Perey.

Gd   Gadolinium

Gadolinium, named after Johan Gadolin (1760–1852), Swiss mineralogist

Symbol: Gd	**Relative Density:** 7.898
Atomic Number: 64	**Melting or Fusing Point:**
Relative Atomic Mass: 157.25	1311°C (2392°F)
Valency: 3	**Boiling Point:** 3233°C
Element Type: Transitional,	(5851°F)
rare-earth, lanthanide	**Isotopes:** Most common
series	is ^{158}Gd
Group: Transitional **Period:** 6	**Allotropes:** Not known

GADOLINIUM is a rare-earth metal from the lanthanide series. It is a silver-white transitional element which exists in small amounts in nature, but only in its oxide form within ores such as gadolinite, bastnaesite and monazite. It is also a product of nuclear fission. The oxide was first isolated in 1880 by Swiss chemist, Jean de Marignac (1817–94), and then again in 1886 by French chemist, Paul Lecoq de Boisbaudran, who is sometimes credited with its discovery, though it is named after the Swiss mineralogist, Gadolin. Gadolinium is used in some electronic components and alloys that are designed to tolerate extremely high temperatures. It is also very good at absorbing neutrons, making it an important substance in nuclear reactors.

Gadolinium is an important element in the nuclear industry.

Gallium

Ga

Gallium, Latin for 'cock' as a translation of French *coq*, as in Lecoq, from the discoverer's name

Symbol: Ga
Atomic Number: 31
Relative Atomic Mass: 69.72
Valency: 2, 3
Element Type: Metal
Group: III **Period:** 4
Relative Density: 5.9

Melting or Fusing Point:
29.78°C (85.60°F)
Boiling Point: 2403°C (4357°F)
Isotopes: Most common
is ^{69}Ga
Allotropes: Not known

GALLIUM is a metal element with such a low melting point, being just above room temperature yet below body temperature, that it turns to liquid in the hand. It is grey and lustrous in appearance. Russian chemist, Dmitri Mendeleyev predicted its existence in 1869 to fill a blank space on his newly devised periodic table. It was duly discovered using spectroscopy in 1875 by French chemist, Paul Lecoq de Boisbaudran. Its main sources are the mineral ore for aluminium, bauxite

Mendeleyev predicted gallium's existence in 1869.

and various zinc ores. Gallium has various uses. In the form of gallium arsenide crystals it is used as a semiconductor material for microelectronics, where it conducts electrons far better than silicon. It is also used in some lasers and thermometers.

Ge

Germanium

Germanium, named after Germany

Symbol: Ge	**Melting or Fusing Point:**
Atomic Number: 32	937°C (1719°F)
Relative Atomic Mass: 72.59	**Boiling Point:** 2830°C
Valency: 4	(5126°F)
Element Type: Metalloid	**Isotopes:** Most common
Group: IV **Period:** 4	is ^{74}Ge
Relative Density: 5.35	**Allotropes:** Not known

GERMANIUM is one of the elements whose existence Dmitri Mendeleyev predicted in 1869. It was eventually discovered in 1886 by German chemist, Clemens Winkler (1838–1904), who named it after his country. It is a metalloid element with a brittle, crystalline appearance and greyish-white colour. The term metalloid, or semimetal, is used to describe elements that

display some, but not all, the properties of metals. They thus fall somewhere between metals and non-metals. Germanium belongs to the silicon group and possesses some properties valued in the manufacture of semiconductor devices such as microelectronic resistors and rectifiers. Germanium can be obtained as a by-product of the smelting of certain mineral ores for zinc, and as a product of the combustion of particular coals.

Germanium is produced in the combustion of certain coals.

Gold   Au

Gold, Old English word for the element

Symbol: Au. From Latin *aurum* meaning 'gold'	**Relative Density:** 19.3
Atomic Number: 79	**Melting or Fusing Point:** 1062°C (1945°F)
Valency: 1, 3	**Boiling Point:** 2800°C (5072°F)
Relative Atomic Mass: 196.9665	**Isotopes:** Most common is ^{197}Au
Element Type: Transitional	**Allotropes:** Not known
Group: Transitional **Period:** 6	

GOLD has been known to humanity since ancient times. It is a transitional, lustrous yellow element which occurs naturally in its native or free elemental state. It is sometimes found as nuggets but more usually as veins within minerals such as quartz. The gold 'dust' panned for in rivers is small particles of gold that have been transported and deposited by water erosion. The gold accumulates because it is heavier than the surrounding mineral fragments. Gold does not dissolve or chemically react. It is an easily worked substance because it is soft and malleable, but it is also fairly weak in pure form. For this reason, manufactured 'gold' is usually an alloy containing other elements such as silver and copper. The value in carats describes the proportion of gold in an alloy (24 carat being pure gold).

Gold is used to make currency, medals and jewellery as it is durable.

As well as being used to make jewellery, gold has long been used as a form of international currency because it is valued for its rarity and beauty, as well as its durability. Gold can be hammered into extremely thin sheets of leaf that can be used for embellishing objects such as picture frames and statues. Industrially, gold also has various important uses. Colloidal gold film can be used to tint glass, and gold is sometimes used in electronics where non-corrosive contacts are essential. In the field of medicine, gold is often used for making replacement teeth, while the radioactive isotope ^{198}Au is used in radiotherapy because it has a relatively safe half-life of 2.7 days.

Gold is mined and turned into bars for storage.

Hafnium   Hf

Hafnium, after *Hafnia* which is Latin for Copenhagen

Symbol: Hf	**Relative Density:** 13.31
Atomic Number: 72	**Melting or Fusing Point:**
Relative Atomic Mass: 178.49	2227°C (4041°F)
Valency: 4	**Boiling Point:** 4602°C (8316°F)
Element Type: Transitional	**Isotopes:** Most common
Group: Transitional	is ^{180}Hf
Period: 6	**Allotropes:** Not known

HAFNIUM was discovered in 1923 by Dirk Coster and George von Hevesy (1885–1966). It is a transitional element with a bright silvery appearance. The element is very similar to zirconium in its properties and accordingly is found in association with zirconium ores, such as zircon. Hafnium has been found to be a good absorber of neutrons, leading to its use as a moderator in control rods for nuclear reactors. It is also used in the manufacture of the filaments for electric light bulbs. The transitional elements, of which hafnium is one, have incomplete inner electron shells to their atoms.

Light-bulb filaments can be made from hafnium.

They typically have variable valencies so that their power to combine with other elements varies and is therefore not reliable in chemical reactions.

Hs

Hassium

Hassium, after *Hassias*, Latin for Hess, the German state

Symbol: Hs	**Relative Density:** Not known
Atomic Number: 108	**Melting or Fusing Point:**
Relative Atomic Mass: 269	Not known
Element Type: Transitional,	**Boiling Point:** Not known
rare-earth, actinide series	**Isotopes:** ^{265}Hs (half-life
Valency: Not known	1.8 milliseconds)
Group: Transitional **Period:** 7	**Allotropes:** Not known

HASSIUM is one of the transuranic rare-earth elements
from the actinide series. It was initially named 'unniloctium'
due to its atomic number, following its discovery in 1984 by
a German team of scientists led by Peter Armbruster and
Gottfried Münzenber. Hassium
was artificially created by
bombarding a lead isotope with
the nuclei of an iron isotope in a
particle accelerator. Isotope ^{265}Hs
has a half-life of just 1.8 milliseconds
or 1.8 thousandths of a second.
Because only a few atoms of
hassium have ever been created
and they can exist for only a split
second, it is of no practical value.
Its sole use is to demonstrate the
possibility of its own existence.

*The German state of Hess gives its
name to this element.*

Helium

He

Helium, from Latin *helio*, meaning 'of the sun'

Symbol: He	**Relative Density:** 0.178
Atomic Number: 2	**Melting or Fusing Point:**
Relative Atomic Mass: 4.0026	-272.2°C (-458°F)
Element Type: Gas,	**Boiling Point:** -268.9°C
non-metal	(-452.02°F)
Valency: 0	**Isotopes:** Single ^{4}He
Group: 0 **Period:** 1	**Allotropes:** Single

HELIUM is a gaseous non-metallic element and a member of the noble gases, meaning that it is inert or unreactive, as well as being invisible to the naked eye and odourless. The element was discovered in 1868 by three scientists independently, following the invention of spectroscopy which revealed its presence in the sun; hence its name. The scientists were French physicist Jules Janssen (1824–1907), British astronomer Norman Lockyer (1836–1920) and British chemist Edward Frankland (1825–99). It was in 1895 that Swedish chemist Per Cleve (1840–1905) showed helium to be present in the mineral clevite, and that Scottish chemist Sir William Ramsay isolated it from air, where it represents 0.0005% by volume.

Helium, mixed with oxygen, produces 'artificial air' for divers.

Helium is the second most abundant element in the universe. It is the waste product of the nuclear-fusion process in stars as they convert hydrogen into helium and energy. It also possesses the lowest melting and boiling points of all the elements. Helium has a number of uses for humans. It is the gas used to fill airships, and meteorological and party balloons because it is the lightest element after hydrogen. It is also used as a medium for producing 'artificial air' where it is mixed with oxygen for scuba and deep-sea divers. Its inert quality is also utilised in industries where oxidation has to be avoided, such as welding and other metallurgical processes. Liquid helium is also used in research on the properties of matter at very low temperatures since it has the lowest boiling point of any known liquid.

Helium is used in airships and balloons as it is the lightest element after hydrogen.

Holmium

Ho

Holmium, after New Latin *Holmia* meaning Stockholm

Symbol: Ho

Atomic Number: 67

Relative Atomic Mass: 164.93

Valency: 3

Element Type: Transitional, Rrare-earth, lanthanide series

Group: Transitional **Period:** 6

Relative Density: 8.803

Melting or Fusing Point: 1470°C (2680°F)

Boiling Point: 2720°C (4930°F)

Isotopes: Most common is ^{165}Ho

Allotropes: Not known

Stockholm, the city after which holmium was named.

HOLMIUM is one of the rare-earth elements from the lanthanide series, found chiefly in the ore minerals gadolinite and monazite, which are the same ores for various other similar elements. Its presence within monazite was first detected spectroscopically in 1878 by Swiss chemists, Jacques-Louis Soret and Marc Fontaine, though it was identified again in 1879 by Swedish chemist, Per Teodor Cleve, who subsequently named the element after Stockholm. Holmium is not used very often commercially, but its compounds have highly magnetic properties, giving them specialised applications in the electronics and engineering industries. Most lanthanides are very similar to one another in characteristics, so it makes economic sense to make use of those that are more readily available – and therefore less expensive to acquire – except when they are required for a use that depends on their precise atomic characteristics.

H

Hydrogen

Hydrogen, from French *hydrogène* which translates as 'water generator', due to water being the product of its combustion with oxygen

Symbol: H
Atomic Number: 1
Relative Atomic Mass: 1.00797
Valency: 1
Element Type: Gas, non-metal
Group: I Period: 1

Relative Density: 0.0899
Melting or Fusing Point: -259.1°C (-434.2°F)
Boiling Point: -252.9°C (-423.2°F)
Isotopes: Most common is ^1H
Allotropes: Single

This shipyard welder relies on hydrogen to produce welding flames.

HYDROGEN is the most abundant element in the universe. It accounts for over three-quarters of the mass of all matter. Discovered in 1766 by British scientist, Henry Cavendish (1731–1810), his original name for the gaseous element was 'inflammable air'. The name hydrogen was settled on eventually though, as it alluded to the element's ability to generate water when burned with oxygen. Cavendish demonstrated that water was a compound in 1781.

Although a gas on Earth, unless part of a compound, hydrogen exists in liquid and solid forms elsewhere in the universe, due to the low temperatures and high gravitational pressures in other places.

The gas has been used as a buoyancy medium in balloons and airships in the past, but its flammable nature gave it a bad reputation leading to its being replaced by noble or inert gases which are a lot safer. Where heat and energy are required, however, hydrogen has come into its own. It is used for producing welding flames and as a fuel for propelling rockets into orbit. The hydrogen bomb works on the same principle as the sun and other stars. Thermonuclear release of energy is the result of hydrogen nuclei undergoing nuclear fusion to become helium nuclei and discarding leftover subatomic particles in the form of heat, light and radiation.

Deuterium and tritium are hydrogen isotopes. The former is a stable isotope with a mass approximately twice that of the usual isotope, the latter is a radioactive isotope with a mass three times that of the usual isotope. Many organic compounds include hydrogen in their make-up, so, along with water, it is essential for all life on earth.

Hydrogen is a fuel used to propel some rockets into orbit.

In
Indium

Indium, derived from indigo, alluding to its spectral colour

Symbol: In	**Melting or Fusing Point:**
Atomic Number: 49	156.6°C (313.9°F)
Relative Atomic Mass: 114.82	**Boiling Point:** 2080°C
Valency: 3	(3776°F)
Element Type: Metal	**Isotopes:** Most common
Group: III **Period:** 5	is ^{115}In
Relative Density: 7.31	**Allotropes:** Not known

INDIUM is a rare silvery-white metal. It is obtained chiefly from ore minerals for zinc, with which it combines in trace amounts. The element is a soft, malleable and ductile metal, yet it is resistant to abrasion, making it a desirable coating for components made from other substances. It is also used in low melting-point alloys for specialised applications and it makes a very good reflective surface behind mirrored glass. The metal is sometimes used in semiconductor devices for microelectronics and as a wetting medium for glass. Indium was discovered in 1863 by two German metallurgical chemists, Ferdinand Reich (1799–1882) and Hieronymous Richter (1824–98). They identified it spectroscopically by the characteristic paired indigo lines that gave the element its name.

Indium makes an excellent reflective surface behind mirrored glass.

Iodine

Iodine, derived from Greek word *iôdês* meaning rust-coloured, but often mistaken for *ion* meaning violet-coloured, because of confusion between the element and its compounds

Symbol: I
Atomic Number: 53
Relative Atomic Mass: 126.9
Valency: 1, 3, 5, 7
Element Type: Non-metal
Group: VII **Period:** 5
Relative Density: 4.93
Melting or Fusing Point: 113.5°C (236.3°F)

Boiling Point: 184.4°C (363.9°F), partially sublimes
Isotopes: Most common is ^{127}I, radioactive ^{131}I (half-life 8 days)
Allotropes: Not known

IODINE is variously described as a blue-black liquid or a crystalline element. It does actually melt from crystals into a liquid when heated, emitting a violet-coloured vapour due to partial sublimation. As with other members of the halogen group its vapours are unpleasant to inhale, its odour being similar to that of chlorine gas. It is not found as a pure element in nature because it reacts with other elements to form

Iodine is isolated from seawater in the form of its salts.

compounds, though it is the least reactive of the halogen group. It is isolated from seawater or brine in the form of its salts which are known specifically as iodides and more generally as halides. Iodine was discovered in 1811 by a French chemist called Bernard Courtois (1777–1838) but his discovery was followed closely in 1813 by that of two others, Charles Désormes (1777–1862) and Nicolas Clément (1779–1841).

Iodine is essential to health, being a constituent of thyroxine, a hormone vital for the functioning of the thyroid gland. Even though required only in trace amounts, its absence results in an iodine deficiency condition known as goitre or hyperthyroidism.

Iodoform is a yellowish crystal used as an antiseptic, made by heating iodine with alcohol. In solution iodine is a rust-brown colour, giving the element its name. The salt, silver iodide, is light sensitive and used in photography. Iodine has a dangerous radioactive isotope – ^{131}I. A product of nuclear fission, it can find its way to the thyroid gland and do irreparable damage, even though it has a half-life of only eight days.

Iodine in specimen glasses (left to right): its crystals give off a violet vapour when heated; dissolved in potassium iodide solution; in carbon disulphide.

Iridium

Ir

Iridium, from Latin for *iridis* meaning rainbow, as the element produces an array of colours when dissolving in acids

Symbol: Ir
Atomic Number: 77
Relative Atomic Mass: 192.2
Valency: 3, 4
Element Type: Transitional
Group: Transitional **Period:** 6
Relative Density: 22.42

Melting or Fusing Point: 2410°C (4370°F)
Boiling Point: 4130°C (7466°F)
Isotopes: Most common is ^{193}Ir
Allotropes: Not known

IRIDIUM has the distinction of being the most corrosion-resistant metallic transitional element. It is similar to platinum in many respects and even occurs within platinum ore minerals. There is a naturally occurring alloy called osmiridium which contains osmium, iridium, platinum, ruthenium and rhodium. All five elements are therefore found in their native or free state, since an alloy is not a chemical compound, but a structurally bonded substance. Iridium was discovered in 1804 by British chemist Smithson Tennant (1761–1815) who named it with reference to its iridescence when dissolved in acids. The element is very hard and brittle in pure form, giving its alloys very desirable properties, useful for the high-precision components of watches, surgical instruments, pen tips, electrical contacts and so on.

Iridium alloys are used in pen nibs.

Fe

Iron

Iron, from Old English *irên*

Symbol: Fe. Abbreviation of Latin *ferrum* meaning iron	**Relative Density:** 7.86
Atomic Number: 26	**Melting or Fusing Point:** 1535°C (2795°F)
Relative Atomic Mass: 55.847	**Boiling Point:** 2750°C (4982°F)
Valency: 2, 3	
Element Type: Transitional	**Isotopes:** Most common is ^{56}Fe
Group: Transitional	
Period: 4	**Allotropes:** Not known

IRON is one of the elements most familiar to mankind. It has been known since antiquity and gave rise to one of the seminal periods in human history – the Iron Age. The element is fairly hard, yet malleable and ductile, especially when heated, making it a very useful material for making many tools, weapons and machine components. It is also very common, being the second most abundant metallic element after aluminium, enabling whole civilisations to be founded on iron industries. Iron can be combined with various elements to form steels. When combined with non-metallic elements, such as carbon, manganese, silicon, sulphur or phosphorous, the steel is not, strictly speaking, an alloy.

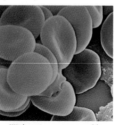

Without iron, oxygen could not be transported in the blood's haemoglobin.

True alloy steels include metallic elements such as nickel, chromium, manganese, vanadium and molybdenum. However, in both cases, the iron acquires desirable new properties, including added strength and toughness, greater hardness and wear resistance, and in the case of stainless steel, resistance to tarnishing and corrosion.

Iron occurs in various forms in nature. Its mineral ores include haematite and magnetite, which are both iron oxides. The element does occasionally occur as a free or native metal, as long as it is not in contact with water and oxygen, since it will rust into its oxides quite readily. Meteorites often contain native iron. The red blood cells of animals contains a molecule called haemoglobin which transports oxygen around the body from the lungs. Iron is an essential component of haemoglobin and a deficiency results in a low red blood cell count, called anaemia.

The Iron Bridge over the River Severn, Shropshire.

Kr

Krypton

Krypton, from Greek *kryptos* meaning hidden

Symbol: Kr	**Relative Density:** 3.73
Atomic Number: 36	**Melting or Fusing Point:**
Relative Atomic Mass: 83.8	-156.6°C (-249.9°F)
Valency: 0	**Boiling Point:** -152.3°C
Element Type: Gas,	(-242.1°F)
non-metal	**Isotopes:** Most common
Group: 0	is ^{84}Kr, also ^{86}Kr
Period: 4	**Allotropes:** Single

KRYPTON is one of the noble gaseous, non-metallic elements. It is invisible to the eye and has no odour or taste. It is present in the air, but only in trace quantities, making up just one ten-thousandth of 1%, by volume. The element was discovered in 1898, along with neon and xenon, by Scottish chemists Sir William Ramsay and Morris Travers (1872–1961). It was isolated by the fractional distillation of air, which is the way it is still obtained. Fractional distillation involves the cooling of air into liquid form and then carefully controlling an increase in temperature so that each of the fractions (component elements) is boiled off and collected one by one. This happens at -152.3°C (-242.1°F) in the case of krypton.

Krypton has found a number of commercial uses, similar to the other noble gases in its group. It is used to fill the tubes of fluorescent lamps where it emits a white light. During the Cold War between the US and USSR, krypton became an espionage tool as it has a radioactive isotope which is a product of nuclear reactors. Scientists from the US were employed to measure increases in the quantity of atmospheric krypton and calculate the amount of nuclear activity going on behind the 'Iron Curtain' by subtracting the quantity naturally known to exist and the amounts generated by non-communist nations. Krypton is also used in lasers and for pneumatically controlling electronic heart valves.

Krypton is used commercially in fluorescent lamps and lasers.

La   Lanthanum

Lanthanum, after Greek *lanthanein* meaning to 'lie unseen'

Symbol: La	**Relative Density:** 6.17
Atomic Number: 57	**Melting or Fusing Point:**
Relative Atomic Mass:	920°C (1688°F)
138.9055	**Boiling Point:** 3454°C
Valency: 3	(6249°F)
Element Type: Transitional,	**Isotopes:** Most common is
rare-earth, lanthanide	^{139}La, there is also a
series	radioactive isotope
Group: Transitional **Period:** 6	**Allotropes:** Not known

LANTHANUM is the first in the lanthanide series of rare-earth elements. It is a silver-white metallic element, found in the mineral ores monazite and bastnaesite. The element is soft, malleable and ductile, making it a useful ingredient in certain alloys for specialist electronic applications, though it is also highly reactive and needs to be kept under argon or a similar noble gas to prevent oxidation. It is also used in pyrophoric alloys which spark or ignite very readily when scratched or abraded, such as those used for the flints of cigarette lighters. It was discovered in 1839 by Swedish chemist Carl Mosander. When combined with glass it gives camera lenses a very desirable refractive, or light-bending, quality.

When combined with glass, lanthanum improves camera lenses.

Lawrencium

Lr

Lawrencium, after US physicist
Ernest Lawrence (1901–58)

Symbol: Lr	**Melting or Fusing Point:** Not known
Atomic Number: 103	**Boiling Point:** Not known
Relative Atomic Mass: 262	**Isotopes:** ^{257}Lr (half-life 4.3
Valency: 3	seconds), ^{256}Lr (half-life
Element Type: Transitional, rare-earth, actinide series	27 seconds)
Group: Transitional **Period:** 7	**Allotropes:** Not known
Relative Density: 260	

LAWRENCIUM was produced artificially, and so discovered, in 1961 by the team led by Glenn Seaborg and Albert Ghiorso at the University of California, Berkeley. It was made by bombarding a californium isotope with the nuclei of boron. Only trace amounts of the element have ever been made, but that is enough to officially identify it as element 103. Bombardment of particles is carried out in an apparatus called a particle accelerator or collider. It is an evacuated chamber in which alternating electric fields are produced. Particles enter as the field is increasing or decreasing, depending on whether they are negative or positive particles. The effect is to speed them up and so increase their energy, making them capable of collision with other particles with enough force to create new elements.

Noble prize winner, Dr Ernest Lawrence, was a nuclear fission pioneer.

Lead

Pb

Lead, an Old English word

Symbol: Pb, from Latin *plumbum* meaning 'lead'
Atomic Number: 82
Relative Atomic Mass: 207.19
Valency: 2, 4
Element Type: Metal
Group: IV **Period:** 6

Relative Density: 11.35
Melting or Fusing Point: 327.5°C (621.5°F)
Boiling Point: 1740°C (3164°F)
Isotopes: Most common is ^{208}Pb
Allotropes: Not known

LEAD has been known to humanity since ancient times. It does, on occasion, occur as a free or native metal, but more usually it is held in compounds within ore minerals such as galena, cerussite and anglesite. The element lead is the final stable product after the five stages of decay of the element uranium: uranium, thorium, radium, radon, polonium and

Lead ingots before casting or being alloyed with other metals.

lead. Lead is a dark-grey lustrous metal, but its surface dulls very quickly with oxidation, though it is not a very reactive element. It is a soft, weak substance but has a low melting point, making it convenient for casting into useful objects, especially when alloyed with other elements to make it tougher. Pewter is an alloy of lead and tin, with the occasional addition of copper and antimony depending on requirements. Lead used to be used frequently for making kitchen utensils, salvers and drinking vessels. It is an accumulative poison when it enters the body via lead water pipes for example, but it is thought to be safe in alloy form. Smelting lead once caused physical and mental illness, so precautions are now taken.

Vast quantities of lead are required commercially. Batteries, especially those in vehicles, use enormous amounts of lead, as do the roofing and plumbing trades, where it is used in the form of lead sheet and solder respectively. It also makes a very effective radiation shield and is used in this way to protect hospital staff from exposure to X-rays as well as in cladding for nuclear reactors. Lead was formerly used as an anti-knock in petrol. To reduce levels of pollution, unleaded petrol was developed and is now used in most modern vehicles.

Lead is usually found as a compound within ore minerals such as galena.

Li

Lithium

Lithium, from Greek for stone – *lithos*

Symbol: Li	**Relative Density:** 0.543
Atomic Number: 3	**Melting or Fusing Point:**
Relative Atomic Mass: 6.941	180.5°C (356.9°F)
Valency: 1	**Boiling Point:** 1347°C
Element Type: Metal, alkali	(2456.6°F)
Group: I	**Isotopes:** Most stable is ^7Li
Period: 2	**Allotropes:** Not known

LITHIUM has the distinction of being the lightest of all the metal elements. Like sodium and potassium it will float in water, but not for long as it is highly reactive, producing its hydroxide in the process. It is a soft, ductile, silvery coloured metal in pure form, but it tarnishes to its oxide very quickly. It also burns with a very bright white light at 200°C (392°F).

The element is found in the mineral ores spodumene and lepidolite – a very complex silicate, sometimes called lithia mica. Lithium was actually discovered in 1817 by a Swedish student of chemistry, Johan Arfwedson (1792–1841); however it was not isolated and named until 1818 by his tutor, Jöns Berzelius.

Various uses have been found for lithium. It is used in

Trace amounts of lithium oxide are found in mineral water.

Light, strong and hard, lithium alloys are used in aircraft components.

alloys where light weight is a particular requirement. For example, it is used in aircraft components where low weight combined with strength and hardness are crucial factors. It is also used in the glass industry and for vitreous ceramic glazes. The element can be found in some batteries and lithium grease. Some lithium salt compounds have been discovered to be useful in combating the symptoms of clinical illnesses and manic depression. Lithia or lithium oxide is a substance used as a drying agent because it is hygroscopic, meaning that it readily absorbs water vapour. It also absorbs carbon dioxide. Lithia is often present in trace amounts in mineral water. Lithium's readiness to oxidise makes it a useful reducing agent for certain chemical processes.

Lu Lutetium

Lutetium, sometimes Lutecium, after *Lûtêtia*,
the Ancient Latin name for Paris

Symbol: Lu	**Group:** Transitional **Period:** 6
Atomic Number: 71	**Relative Density:** 9.842
Relative Atomic Mass: 174.97	**Melting or Fusing Point:**
Valency: 3	1656°C (3013°F)
Element Type: Transitional,	**Boiling Point:** 3315°C (5999°F)
rare-earth, lanthanide	**Isotopes:** Most common
series	is ^{175}Lu
	Allotropes: Not known

Lutetium is used in fertilisers.

LUTETIUM is the last in the lanthanide series of rare-earth elements. It is a silver-white metallic element found in the mineral ore monazite. It was first discovered in 1906 by French chemist Georges Urbain (1872–1938) and then again, independently, in 1907 by Austrian chemist Carl von Welsbach (1858–1929). It was named after Paris, the home town of Urbain. It has a few commercial uses in the chemical industry. It is used as a catalyst in some processes, for example as a cracking agent for the breakdown of petroleum molecules into smaller molecules for use in petrochemical products, such as polymers, detergents, solvents and fertilisers.

Magnesium

Mg

Magnesium, from New Latin *magnesia*

Symbol: Mg
Atomic Number: 12
Relative Atomic Mass: 24.312
Valency: 2
Element Type: Metal, alkaline-Earth
Group: II **Period:** 3

Relative Density: 1.738
Melting or Fusing Point: 648.8°C (1200°F)
Boiling Point: 1090°C (1994°F)
Isotopes: Most common is ^{24}Mg
Allotropes: Not known

MAGNESIUM is one of the alkaline-earth metals. It is a lightweight, silver-white metal which is ductile and malleable. One of its most well-known characteristics is its readiness to ignite and burn with an extremely bright white flame as it oxidises. Magnesium was discovered in 1808 by British scientist, Sir Humphry Davy. It is isolated from mineral ores, such as magnesite and dolomite. The element is actually the eighth most abundant in the Earth's crust, since its compounds – magnesium silicate, chloride and carbonate – make up a significant amount of the asthenosphere.

The combustible nature of magnesium is utilised in flares and fireworks.

Traces of magnesium are essential for plant and animal life.

The oxide of magnesium is an ingredient of antacid remedies due to its alkalinity. It is also used for making the insulating lining bricks in furnaces because it is very stable and unaffected by high temperatures. The metal itself is used in flashbulbs, flares, pyrotechnics and incendiary devices as a result of its combustible nature. It is also used for making high-strength but low-mass alloys for application in aircraft, missiles and rockets. Magnesium plays an important biological role. It is essential in trace amounts for the life of animals and plants. In animals, including humans, it serves various purposes such as building bones, controlling metabolism and converting proteins, fats and sugars into energy. In plants it is an essential component of chlorophyll, the green pigment responsible for photosynthesis. Hydrated magnesium sulphate is taken as a purgative called Epsom salts, which acts as a laxative.

Manganese

Mn

Manganese, corruption of Latin *magnesia* meaning magnesium, another element

Symbol: Mn
Atomic Number: 25
Relative Atomic Mass: 54.938
Valency: 2, 3, 4, 6, 7
Element Type: Transitional
Group: Transitional **Period:** 4
Relative Density: 7.2

Melting or Fusing Point:
1244°C (2271°F)
Boiling Point: 1962°C
(3564°F)
Isotopes: Most common
is ^{55}Mn
Allotropes: Not known

MANGANESE is a transitional metallic element and very different from magnesium, with which it sometimes gets confused. It is actually quite similar to iron, having an adjacent atomic number. It is a greyish lustrous substance and, like iron, it rusts to give a brown oxide. It is softer than iron, however, and it is not magnetic. The element is obtained from mineral ores such as manganite, pyrosulite, psilomelane, rhodocrosite and hausmannite. It also occurs as manganese nodules that litter the floor of the oceans in places.

Chemical industries use manganese for making paints.

In fact, manganese is present in small quantities in most rocks, whether they are igneous, sedimentary or metamorphic. Manganese was discovered in 1774 by Swedish mineralogist, Johan Gahn (1745–1818).

In combination with iron, manganese is used for making alloy steels, where it acts as a cleanser as well as a toughener. Some ferromagnetic alloys also use manganese. It will also alloy well with aluminium and copper. Chemical industries use manganese for making paints, fertilisers and petrol additives amongst other things. Manganese dioxide is a component of some dry batteries, where it oxidises the hydrogen produced into water, thereby functioning as a depolariser. Manganese is a vital trace element in animal nutrition. In humans it helps in building bones, metabolising glucose, synthesising the brain neurotransmitter dopamine, and it acts as an antioxidant. Manganese is grouped with two other elements, technetium and rhenium. It has most in common with rhenium in terms of chemical properties, though rhenium is almost three times as heavy.

Manganese is one of the additives found in petrol.

Meitnerium

Mt

Meitnerium, after Lise Meitner (1878–1968),
Austrian physicist

Symbol: Mt
Atomic Number: 109
Relative Atomic Mass: 266
Valency: Not known
Element Type: Transitional,
rare-earth, actinide series
Group: Transitional **Period:** 7

Relative Density: Not known
Melting or Fusing Point:
Not known
Boiling Point: Not known
Isotopes: ^{266}Mt
Allotropes: Not known

MEITNERIUM is one of the more recently discovered elements. It is one of the transactinide, transuranic rare-earth elements, that have been created artificially using a particle accelerator. It was produced in 1982 by bombarding a bismuth isotope with the nuclei of an iron isotope.

The element meitnerium was named after the Austrian physicist Lise Meitner (above left).

Radioactive meitnerium-266 has a half-life of 3.4 milliseconds. Radioactive elements decay in jumps of two because of the way that they lose elementary particles from their nuclei. Thus, meitnerium becomes bohrium which in turn becomes dubnium and so on. Each stage is described as the 'parent' element becoming the 'daughter' element. Meitnerium has only ever been created in trace amounts of several atoms, so nothing is known of its appearance, and it has no known applications.

Md Mendelevium

Mendelevium, named after the man who invented the periodic table, Dmitri Mendeleyev (1834–1907)

Symbol: Md
Atomic Number: 101
Relative Atomic Mass: 256
Valency: 2, 3
Element Type: Transitional, rare-earth, actinide series
Group: Transitional **Period:** 7

Relative Density: Not known
Melting or Fusing Point: Not known
Boiling Point: Not known
Isotopes: ^{256}Md, ^{258}Md
Allotropes: Not known

MENDELEVIUM was first created, and so discovered, in 1955. This was done in a particle accelerator, one atom at a time, by bombarding an isotope of einsteinium with alpha particles. There are two known isotopes: ^{258}Md has a half-life of around 60 days, while ^{256}Md has a half-life of a mere 76 minutes. Even this is long-lived compared with other

Dmitri Ivanovich Mendeleyev, creator of the periodic table.

radioactive rare-earth elements. The Berkeley team, led by Albert Ghiorso and Glenn Seaborg, was the first to succeed with mendelevium, which was named after the man who created the periodic table, Dmitri Mendeleyev, a Russian chemist. The element is similar in chemical properties to thulium, being a silver-white heavy metallic substance. It has no commercial uses.

Mercury
Hg

Mercury, also called quicksilver, from Latin *mercurius*, meaning the messenger of the gods or the planet Mercury

Symbol: Hg. Abbreviation for Latin word *hydrargyrum* meaning 'silver water'

Atomic Number: 80

Relative Atomic Mass: 200.59

Valency: 1, 2

Element Type: Transitional, liquid metallic

Group: Transitional **Period:** 6

Relative Density: 13.6

Melting or Fusing Point: -38.87°C (-37.97°F)

Boiling Point: 356.58°C (673.84°F)

Isotopes: Most common is ^{202}Hg

Allotropes: Not known

MERCURY is well-known for being the only one of the metallic elements which is a liquid at room temperature, i.e. 22°C (71°F). Its existence has been known of since the earliest times as it occurs in nature as a free or native element, although its most common source is the mineral ore cinnabar, mercuric sulphide – HgS – which contains 86% mercury. The element was formerly used in the recovery of gold and silver from their mineral ores and as a reflective surface for mirrors. When alloyed with other metals the product is described as an amalgam. Silver-mercury amalgam is used in dentistry for tooth fillings.

Liquid at room temperature, mercury is used in barometers. The tube in this pocket instrument, made in 1839, contains a mixture of air, spirit and mercury.

When not alloyed, mercury and its compounds are cumulative poisons or toxins which can have some profound effects on organisms. If they enter a food chain then the species higher up will accumulate dangerous amounts of mercury in their body tissues, leading to symptoms such as organ failure, brain damage and birth defects. The compound dimethylmercury was one of several such twentieth-century toxins which entered the food chain. The pollution was caused by industrial waste containing dimethylmercury being discharged into rivers and seas.

The element is used in its pure form for filling thermometers, barometers and fluid switches. The poisonous vapours produced

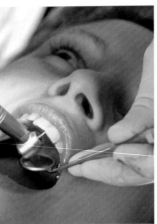

by heating mercury are used in mercury-vapour lamps, giving off a bluish light. Mercury fulminate is a very unstable mercury compound used as an explosive for filling bomb detonators and artillery percussion caps. Mercuric chloride is a white crystalline poison which has several uses including as a pesticide, antiseptic or preservative.

A silver-mercury amalgam is used in dentistry.

Molybdenum · Mo

Molybdenum, from Latin and Greek words *molybdaena* and *molubdos*, meaning galena (lead ore) and graphite respectively

Symbol: Mo	**Melting or Fusing Point:**
Atomic Number: 42	2610°C (4730°F)
Relative Atomic Mass: 95.94	**Boiling Point:** 5560°C
Valency: 3, 4, 6	(10040°F)
Element Type: Transitional	**Isotopes:** Most common
Group: Transitional **Period:** 5	is ^{98}Mo
Relative Density: 10.22	**Allotropes:** Not known

MOLYBDENUM is a metallic transitional element with a silvery-white lustrous appearance. It is very hard and brittle, with a high melting point, making it very well suited to combining with iron for making tough alloyed steels. Its chief source is the mineral ore molybdenite, which is molybdenum sulphide – MoS_2. It sometimes occurs in hexagonal crystals within rocks. In this form it is very similar to graphite, being metal-grey and cleavable into flexible laminae, hence its name. It does have a bluish-violet tint however. The element was discovered in 1778 by the Swedish chemists Torbern Bergman (1735–84) and Carl William Scheele, who chose its name. It was later isolated in 1781 by fellow Swede, Peter Hjelm (1760–1813). Molybdenum is used in bulb filaments.

Molybdenum is used to make bulb filaments due to its very high melting point.

Nd **Neodymium**

Neodymium, from Latin *neo–didymium* meaning 'new didymium'. Didymium is actually an alloy of the elements neodymium, praseodymium and cerium, but was once thought to be an element in its own right

Symbol: Nd	**Relative Density:** 7.004
Atomic Number: 60	**Melting or Fusing Point:**
Relative Atomic Mass: 144.24	1010°C (1850°F)
Valency: 3	**Boiling Point:** 3068°C
Element Type: Transitional,	(5554°F)
rare-earth, lanthanide	**Isotopes:** Most common
series	is ^{142}Nd
Group: Transitional **Period:** 6	**Allotropes:** Not known

NEODYMIUM is a member of the lanthanide series of rare-earth elements. It is therefore not radioactive in its usual form, though it is toxic. It has the typical, silvery-metallic appearance of the transitionals, but with a tinge of yellow. The element was discovered in 1885 by the Austrian chemist, Carl von Welsbach who isolated its oxide by fractioning a substance known as didymium, which was thought to be an element in its own right but turned out to comprise various other elements including cerium and praseodymium as well as neodymium. The pure element was isolated in 1925. Some neodymium salts have a rose colour and have been used as pigments in glass and vitreous glazes. It is also used in laser materials.

Carl von Welsbach discovered neodymium in 1885.

Neon

Ne

Neon, from Greek *neon* meaning new

Symbol: Ne	**Relative Density:** Not known
Atomic Number: 10	**Melting or Fusing Point:**
Relative Atomic Mass: 20.179	-248.67°C (-415.6°F)
Valency: 0	**Boiling Point:** -246.05°C
Element Type: Gas,	(-410.89°F)
non-metal	**Isotopes:** Most common
Group: 0	is ^{20}Ne
Period: 2	**Allotropes:** Single

NEON is one of the noble gaseous, non-metallic elements. It is inert, invisible, odourless and has no taste. It is so inert that it will only form compounds with other elements under very special laboratory conditions, but even then only for a moment. The gas makes up 0.0018%, or 1.8 thousandths, of the air by volume. It was discovered in 1898 by British chemists Sir William Ramsay and Morris Travers. They achieved its isolation in the same way as for the other noble gases – through the fractional distillation of air.

The most widespread and familiar use for neon is in the ubiquitous fluorescent advertising lighting tube, where it emits an attractive bright

Neon is used in fluorescent advertising tubes.

orange-red glow whilst conducting an electrical current under low pressure. The term 'neon sign' does not, however, necessarily mean that neon is the gas being used since a variety of colours are now available. Neon is also used in gas-filled lasers, particle detectors and Geiger counters – where radiation ionises the gas atoms in a chamber between two electrodes, resulting in pulses of current that can be counted. The noble gases were not known to Dmitri Mendeleyev when he devised the first periodic table. It was not possible to discover them until air could be liquified and then distilled into its component parts. The search was first prompted by a discrepancy between the calculated density of nitrogen from the air and nitrogen obtained chemically. Together, the noble gases account for only about 1% of the volume of air.

The equipment used by Ramsay for studying rare atmospheric gases.

Neptunium

Np

Neptunium, after the planet Neptune, because it comes after uranium, named after Uranus, in the periodic table

Symbol: Np	**Melting or Fusing Point:**
Atomic Number: 93	640°C (1184°F)
Relative Atomic Mass:	**Boiling Point:** 3902°C
237.0482	(7056°F)
Valency: 4, 5, 6	**Isotopes:** Most stable is
Element Type: Transitional,	^{237}Np (half-life 2.2 million
rare-earth, actinide series	years), also ^{239}Np
Group: Transitional **Period:** 7	(half-life 2.35 days)
Relative Density: 20.25	**Allotropes:** Not known

NEPTUNIUM has the distinction of being the first transactinide element to be synthesised in a laboratory. It is a silvery, metallic, radioactive element in the actinide series. It does occur in nature, but only in extremely small amounts within uranium mineral ores, such as pitchblende. It is a natural decay product of neutron-bombarded uranium. Its isotopes are all highly chemically reactive but their half-lives vary considerably, from 2.2 million years in the case of ^{237}Np to 2.35 days in the case of ^{239}Np. Edwin McMillan (1907–91) and Philip Abelson (b. 1913) were the American physicists who first synthesised neptunium, in 1940. Neptunium is also a by-product in nuclear reactors that use uranium for their fuel rods.

Edwin McMillan was one of the scientists to synthesise neptunium.

Ni

Nickel

The name nickel may be derived from *kupfernickel*, the German name for the ore niccolite, translated as 'copper rogue' as it was thought to contain copper. Alternatively from Swedish *kopparnickel* meaning 'false copper' since the ores of the two elements are so similar

Symbol: Ni	**Melting or Fusing Point:**
Atomic Number: 28	1453°C (2647°F)
Relative Atomic Mass: 58.71	**Boiling Point:** 2732°C
Valency: 2, 3	(4950°F)
Element Type: Transitional	**Isotopes:** Most common
Group: Transitional **Period:** 4	is ^{58}Ni
Relative Density: 8.9	**Allotropes:** Not known

NICKEL shares some similarities with copper in terms of chemical and physical properties; the two are adjacent to one another in the periodic table. Their ore minerals are also very similar in appearance, hence the confusion over the origin of the name of element 28. Depending on the story you choose, 'nickel' means either 'rogue' in German or 'false' in Swedish, but both are alluding to the fact that people were fooled by the ore niccolite, thinking that they were smelting copper. The element is a

Swiss centime coins are made from nickel.

relatively hard, yet malleable and ductile substance, with a silver-white metallic appearance. It is an abundant element, for it is combined with iron to form the core of our planet. Like iron, nickel is a ferromagnetic element. Niccolite is in fact a compound of nickel and the element arsenic, as is chloanthite. Other nickel ores are millerite and pentlandite. Niccolite is used in the production of stainless and other steels for specialised uses.

Nickel was discovered in 1751 by Swedish mineralogist, Axel Cronstedt (1722–65), though Saxon miners had already confused its ores with copper's hundreds of years previously. Nickel plate is a thin layer of the element deposited electrolytically onto a surface to protect it from corrosion, as nickel is very unreactive. Nickel's resistance to tarnishing has meant that it has also been a popular substance for making alloys for minting coins. Nickel silver, or German silver, is actually an alloy of zinc, nickel and copper, and it is used for making, amongst other things, tableware and jewellery.

Stainless steel, which contains niccolite, can be used to clad buildings.

Nb

Niobium

Niobium, after Niobe the daughter of Tantalus in Greek mythology. It is also sometimes called columbium, Cb

Symbol: Nb

Atomic Number: 41

Relative Atomic Mass: 92.906

Valency: 3, 5

Element Type: Transitional

Group: Transitional **Period:** 5

Relative Density: 8.57

Melting or Fusing Point: 2468°C (4474°F)

Boiling Point: 4742°C (8568°F)

Isotopes: Most common is ^{93}Nb

Allotropes: Not known

NIOBIUM is named after Niobe, daughter of Tantalus from Greek mythology, because of the element's similarity with the element tantalum, named after Tantalus himself. The name niobium was chosen in 1844 by German chemist, Heinrich Rose (1795–1864), but it was originally called columbium (Cb), when discovered in 1801 by English chemist, Charles Hatchett (1765–1847), after its column-shaped ore crystals. Some metallurgists still use the original name. The element is soft, malleable and ductile with a grey-white metallic appearance. Its main commercial application is as a component of stainless steels and alloys used for high-precision and heat-resistant components in machines such as aircraft and rocket engines. It occurs in nature with tantalum in the ore mineral columbite-tantalite.

Niobium is used as a component of stainless steels – here used in a bus shelter.

Nitrogen   **N**

Nitrogen, after Greek *nitron* meaning 'native soda' or 'nitre' which are names for both potassium nitrate and sodium nitrate. Thus 'nitro' plus 'gen' means 'nitre generator'

Symbol: N

Atomic Number: 7

Relative Atomic Mass: 14.0067

Valency: 3, 5

Element Type: Gas, non-metal

Group: V **Period:** 2

Relative Density: 1.2506

Melting or Fusing Point: -209.86°C (-345.75°F)

Boiling Point: -195.8°C (-320.4°F)

Isotopes: Most common is ^{14}N

Allotropes: Single

NITROGEN is the most common gaseous element in the atmosphere. It accounts for some 78% of the air by volume. It is a colourless and odourless gas, but it is not a noble gas, despite being relatively unreactive. Like the noble gases, it is obtained commercially through the fractional distillation of air. The element was discovered in 1772 by English chemist Daniel Rutherford (1749–1819) and given its name in 1790 by French chemist Jean Chaptal (1756–1832). The nitrate salts, after which the element gets its name, are very useful as they have a wide variety of applications.

Nitrates in the soil are vital for plant life.

Nitre is the collective name for potassium nitrate and sodium nitrate. Potassium nitrate or saltpetre is a naturally occurring mineral which is used for making gunpowder and as a preservative for curing meats. Sodium nitrate, also called Chile saltpetre and nitratine, is also used in the manufacture of explosives. Nitrates in the soil are vital compounds for plants to be able to make protein and nucleic acid molecules. These nitrates may occur naturally, or nitrogen from the air may be 'fixed' into compounds by bacteria that live in the roots of leguminous plants. The use of nitrates as plant fertilisers is widespread, but it can, and frequently does, lead to nitrate pollution, where rain washes the salts into rivers and lakes. The water becomes too enriched with nutrients, causing algae and bacteria to flourish, using up all available oxygen and killing fish and invertebrates. Nitrogen has a variety of other uses in chemicals industries.

Algal bloom caused by over-enrichment of water by nitrates.

Nobelium

No

Nobelium, after Alfred Nobel (1833–96), Swedish scientist

Symbol: No	**Melting or Fusing Point:** Not kown
Atomic Number: 102	
Relative Atomic Mass: 254	**Boiling Point:** Not known
Valency: 2, 3	**Isotopes:** Most stable is ^{254}No (half-life 3 minutes), also ^{255}No (half-life 2.3 seconds)
Element Type: Transitional, rare-earth, actinide series	
Group: Transitional **Period:** 7	
Relative Density: Not known	**Allotropes:** Not known

NOBELIUM is a synthesised, radioactive, rare-earth element from the actinide series of transuranic elements. Named after Swedish pioneering scientist, Alfred Nobel, the element was thought to have been 'discovered' in 1958 by the Albert Ghiorso and Glenn Seaborg team working at the University of California, Berkeley. A claim was made for its discovery at the Nobel Institute in Stockholm in 1957 but this was later shown to be incorrect. Since 1992 it has been recognised by the International Union of Applied Chemistry that a Soviet team at Dubna actually created nobelium first. Nobelium is made by bombarding a curium isotope with the nuclei of a carbon isotope. Seven isotopes have been made in trace amounts. They have no known applications.

Eminent chemist, Alfred Nobel, after whom nobelium was named.

Os

Osmium

Osmium, after Greek *osmê* meaning smelly

Symbol: Os	**Melting or Fusing Point:**
Atomic Number: 76	3045°C (5513°F)
Relative Atomic Mass: 190.2	**Boiling Point:** 5027°C
Valency: 2, 3, 4, 8	(9081°F)
Element Type: Transitional	**Isotopes:** Most common
Group: Transitional **Period:** 6	is ^{192}Os
Relative Density: 22.57	**Allotropes:** Not known

OSMIUM has the distinction of being the densest element, 22.57 times as heavy as water. It is a metallic transitional element with a bluish-white lustre. In nature it is associated with the element platinum and its most common source is the mineral ores of nickel, such as niccolite. The element also occurs as a free or native metal in a naturally occurring alloy called osmiridium, which is a blend of osmium and iridium with traces of platinum, ruthenium and rhodium. Osmium was discovered in 1804 by British chemist Smithson Tennant and given its name because of its penetrating odour. It is used as a chemical catalyst and for making very hard-wearing and heat-resistant alloys for light-bulb filaments, pen tips and so on.

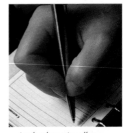

As a hard-wearing alloy, osmium is used to make pen tips.

Oxygen

Oxygen, from Greek *oxys* meaning acid, thus
'oxy' plus 'gen' means 'acid maker'

Symbol: O	**Relative Density:** 1.429
Atomic Number: 8	**Melting or Fusing Point:**
Relative Atomic Mass:	-218.4°C (-361.1°F)
15.9994	**Boiling Point:** -182.96°C
Valency: 2	(-297.3°F)
Element Type: Gas,	**Isotopes:** Most common
non-metal	is ^{16}O
Group: VI	**Allotropes:** Atmospheric
Period: 2	oxygen O_2, ozone O_3

OXYGEN is the most abundant element in the Earth's crust, accounting for approximately 49.2% of its weight. It exists in many compounds and minerals. It also makes up 21% of the air by volume and 33% of the atoms in water. The element is an invisible, odourless and tasteless gas, but it is chemically reactive. It will readily oxidise other reactive elements, especially during combustion. Oxygen was officially discovered in 1774 by British scientist, Joseph Priestley (1733–1804) but it was also 'discovered' in *c.* 1772 independently by Swedish chemist Carl William Scheele.

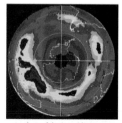

Analysis of the ozone layer reveals dangerously thin areas and even some holes.

The name was chosen in 1777 by French chemist Antoine Lavoisier (1743–94).

Oxygen is essential to life. For a start, no organism could exist without water to lubricate its movements, fill its cells and transport chemicals. Secondly, respiration requires oxygen. Respiration is the breakdown of complex organic substances in cells by oxidation so that their components can be used. The waste product is an oxide of carbon, known as carbon dioxide, which is then expelled from the body. Atmospheric oxygen exists as paired atoms making the allotropic molecule O_2. Solar ultraviolet light and electrical sparks can divide these molecules and create single atoms, O_1. When this happens, single and double atoms quickly combine to form a three-atom molecule of oxygen, which is an allotrope known as ozone, O_3. Ozone is a highly reactive, pale-blue gas which forms a vitally important layer in the upper atmosphere, protecting the Earth's surface from the ultraviolet radiation of the sun.

Oxygen is also used in steel-making, for welding, for life-support systems in medicine and to produce other chemicals.

Carl Scheele conducting experiments to determine the composition of air.

Palladium

Pd

Palladium, after the asteroid Pallas,
itself discovered in 1802

Symbol: Pd	**Melting or Fusing Point:**
Atomic Number: 46	1552°C (2826°F)
Relative Atomic Mass: 106.4	**Boiling Point:** 3140°C (5684°F)
Valency: 2, 4, 6	**Isotopes:** Most common
Element Type: Transitional	is ^{106}Pd
Group: Transitional **Period:** 5	**Allotropes:** Not known
Relative Density: 12.02	

PALLADIUM is a member of the platinum group of transitional metallic elements. It is silvery-white in appearance and is a ductile and malleable substance. It does not tarnish or corrode easily and is used in alloys with gold (white gold) and platinum for making the components of jewellery and surgical equipment, for example. Palladium is also used in catalytic converters and as an electroplating medium. Its main sources are the mineral ores of nickel, where it is usually associated with platinum and sometimes alloyed with it. The element was discovered along with rhodium in 1803 by British scientist William Wollaston (1766–1828). The asteroid Pallas had been discovered in 1802 by German astronomer Heinrich Olbers (1758–1840), hence the name chosen for the new element.

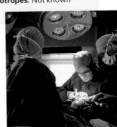

Palladium is used to make surgical equipment.

P **Phosphorus**

Phosphorus, from Greek words *phos* (light) and *pherein* (to bring) giving *phosphoros* (light bringer)

Symbol: P	**Melting or Fusing Point:**
Atomic Number: 15	44.1°C (111.38°F)
Relative Atomic Mass 30.974	**Boiling Point:** 280°C (536°F)
Element Type: Non-metal	**Isotopes:** Most common
Valency: 3, 5	is ^{31}P, also ^{32}P (half-life
Group: V **Period:** 3	14.3 days)
Relative Density: 1.82	**Allotropes:** Black, white
(white), 2.34 (red)	and red

PHOSPHORUS can exist in three allotropic forms: black, white and white. The element was discovered in 1669 by German alchemist Hennig Brand (1630–92) and also described independently in 1680 by the Irish scientist Robert Boyle (1627–91). White phosphorus is a highly reactive white solid which will spontaneously ignite on exposure to air, such is its readiness to oxidise. It is also a toxic substance, which can cause a condition known as phossy jaw, where the lower jaw turns gangrenous as a result of prolonged exposure to phosphorus fumes or

Phosphoric acid is a compound used in the manufacture of soap.

Red phosphorus is used to make chemical fertilisers.

phosphorus pentoxide. Red phosphorus is a less reactive substance which is non-toxic. There is additionally a radioactive phosphorus isotope – ^{32}P – which has a half-life of 14.3 days. It is used in radiotherapy and as a tracer, where it is known as radiophosphorus. Phosphorus is sourced from various phosphate-containing mineral ores, such as apatite and phosphorite. Phosphate rock deposits are very common. Phosphates are the salt compounds of phosphorus.

Phosphates are essential for plants to grow healthy root systems. Phosphorus is also a vital ingredient in biological membranes, such as in cell walls, where it combines to form fatty molecules called phospholipids. Compounds of phosphorus are known generally as phosphides and any chemical process involving the combination of phosphorus with other chemicals is termed phosphoration. Phosphoric acid is a compound used in the manufacture of fertilisers and soap. Red phosphorus is used in the manufacture of insecticides, the heads of matches, fireworks and alloy steels.

Pt

Platinum

Platinum, from Spanish *platina* meaning 'lesser silver'

Symbol: Pt	**Melting or Fusing Point:** 1772°C (3222°F)
Atomic Number: 78	
Relative Atomic Mass: 195.09	**Boiling Point:** 3800°C (6872°F)
Valency: 2, 4	**Isotopes:** Most common is ^{195}Pt
Element Type: Transitional	
Group: Transitional **Period:** 6	**Allotropes:** Not known
Relative Density: 21.45	

PLATINUM is a precious, transitional metallic element. It is chemically unreactive and resistant to tarnishing and corrosion, making it very well suited for alloying with other metallic elements for particular applications. These include jewellery, and tools for dentistry and surgery. The element is very similar to five other metallic transitional elements: iridium, osmium, palladium, rhodium and ruthenium. In fact it is sometimes found as a free or native element along

In 1557 Julius Scaliger described what was probably a platinum alloy.

with the others in a naturally occurring alloy called osmiridium. Platinum is found mainly in the mineral ores of the element nickel, for example niccolite. It is left behind in the refined slimes after electrolysis of nickel and then dissolved into aqua regia, a mixture of hydrochloric and nitric acids. It does sometimes occur in its own ores though, such as sperrylite or platinum arsenide, a white solid with black streaking.

Platinum has an interesting history as it was identified as an element in 1741 by British chemist William Brownrigg (1711–1800), yet it had already been described in 1557 by Italian physician Julius Scaliger (1484–1558). Scaliger knew of it from native or free samples of Spanish origin. Spanish scientist Antonio de Ulloa (1716–95) also described it in 1748, but it is likely that both of the early accounts are actually describing a platinum alloy rather than the pure element. Other commercial uses for platinum include its use for electrical-resistance wiring, electrodes, thermocouples and magnets. It is also used in catalytic converters on the exhaust pipes of vehicles.

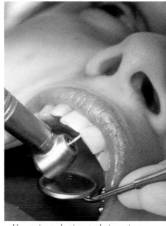

Unreactive and resistant, platinum is used in the manufacture of dentistry tools.

Pu

Plutonium

Plutonium, after the planet Pluto, as the element
was discovered just after neptunium,
named afterplanet Neptune

Symbol: Pu	**Melting or Fusing Point:**
Atomic Number: 94	641°C (1186°F)
Relative Atomic Mass: 244	**Boiling Point:** 3232°C (5850°F)
Valency: 3, 4, 5, 6	**Isotopes:** Most stable
Element Type: Transitional,	is ^{244}Pu (half-life 76
rare-earth, actinide series	million years), also ^{239}Pu
Group: Transitional **Period:** 7	(half-life 24,360 years)
Relative Density: 19.84	**Allotropes:** Not known

*Plutonium is manufactured
synthetically in nuclear reactors.*

PLUTONIUM is a toxic,
radioactive, rare-earth element
from the actinide series. It was
discovered in 1940 by the
Glenn Seaborg-led team at the
University of California,
Berkeley. Plutonium is
manufactured synthetically
by bombarding uranium with
deuterons, which are the nuclei
of deuterium atoms – deuterium
being an isotope of hydrogen –
within nuclear breeder reactors.
The element also occurs
naturally in trace amounts
within uranium ores, such as

itchblende, where it decays into uranium. The isotope ^{239}Pu an undergo fission, so is used as a fuel in nuclear reactors.

A more sinister use for plutonium is in atom bombs, developed before work on hydrogen bombs took place. Atom bombs work on a principle called critical mass. Given a sufficient mass of the fissile fuel, in this case plutonium, a self-sustaining chain reaction begins, because fission occurs naturally in plutonium atoms. In nuclear reactors this reaction is kept in check, so that the energy produced can be used safely to generate electricity via steam turbines. In the case of bombs the reaction is uncontrolled, resulting in a nuclear explosion. Vast amounts of energy, in the forms of heat, light and radiation are emitted as the plutonium atoms split into fragments that recombine into other elements. Plutonium is a dangerous radiological hazard, because it emits high levels of alpha particles, which are the nuclei of helium atoms. They have low penetrative ability but re readily absorbed into bone where they cause ionisation, leading to radiation sickness and leukaemia.

Plutonium was a main ingredient in the atom bomb, the precursor to the hydrogen bomb.

Po

Polonium

Polonium, after *Polonia,* Latin for Poland,
homeland of its discoverer, Marie Curie

Symbol: Po	**Relative Density:** 9.4
Atomic Number: 84	**Melting or Fusing Point:**
Relative Atomic Mass: 209	254°C (489°F)
Valency: 2, 3, 4	**Boiling Point:** 962°C (1764°F)
Element Type: Metalloid,	**Isotopes:** Most stable is
radioactive	^{209}Po (half-life 103 years),
Group: VI	also 26 other isotopes
Period: 6	**Allotropes:** Not known

POLONIUM is a radioactive, metalloid element. It is very rare,
only occurring in trace amounts within uranium ores such as
pitchblende. It has the distinction of being the element with the
most isotopes – it has 27. The element is extremely radioactive,
even giving off a considerable amount of heat when in quantity.
It was the first element to be recognised as radioactive and to
have this phenomenon investigated. It was discovered in 1898
by Pierre and Marie Curie, along with
radium, by analysis of pitchblende
residue, and eventually isolated in
1902. It is 5000 times as radioactive
as radium and undoubtedly
contributed to the death of Marie
Curie by radiation poisoning in 1934.
Neither she nor her husband Pierre
took any precautions against the
element's radioactivity.

*Pierre and Marie Curie
in their Paris laboratory.*

Potassium K

Potassium, after *potassa*, Dutch for potash, which is both potassium carbonate and potassium hydroxide

Symbol: K – after *kalium*, its Latin name	**Relative Density:** 0.86
Atomic Number: 19	**Melting or Fusing Point:** 63.65°C (146.6°F)
Relative Atomic Mass: 39.102	**Boiling Point:** 774°C (1425°F)
Valency: 1	**Isotopes:** Most common is ^{39}K, also ^{40}K (half-life 1.28 x 10^9 years)
Element Type: Metal, alkali	
Group: I	
Period: 4	**Allotropes:** Not known

POTASSIUM is a soft, silver-white, alkali metal element, with a wax-like texture. It was discovered in 1807 by Sir Humphry Davy. After lithium, it is the lightest metal, having a density some 86% that of water. As well as floating on water it will react violently with it, producing potassium hydroxide in the

Potassium bromide is used in photography.

process. In the absence of water it will react with the oxygen in air, producing potassium oxide. Potassium is too reactive to occur in its free or native state. The element is abundant when compounded with other elements in many minerals, especially potassium aluminium silicates. Its main commercial sources are the mineral ores sylvite, carnallite and polyhalite.

Potassium compounds have many uses. Potassium carbonate and potassium hydroxide, both known as potash, are used in the manufacture of soft soaps, detergents, cleansing agents and glass. Potassium bromide is used in photography and as a sedative in medicine. Potassium chlorate is employed in the manufacture of explosives, disinfectants and bleaches. Potassium cyanide is also used in photography. Potassium hydrogen tartrate is a constituent of baking powders, soldering fluxes and laxatives. Potassium nitrate is an ingredient of gunpowder, fertilisers and food preservatives. Potassium permanganate is a dark purple crystal applied in solution as a disinfectant and antiseptic. In addition there is a radioactive isotope (radioisotope) of potassium – ^{40}K (half-life 1.28×10^9 years) – which decays into argon, the isotope ^{40}Ar. The ratio between the two isotopes expresses the age of a potassium-containing mineral and is known as potassium-argon dating.

Sir Humphry Davy discovered potassium in 1807.

Praseodymium Pr

Praseodymium, after Greek *prasios* and *dymium* giving
'leek-green didymium'. Didymium, twin in Greek, is an alloy
of rare-earth metals, once thought to be a single element

Symbol: Pr	**Group:** Transitional **Period:** 6
Atomic Number: 59	**Relative Density:** 6.77
Relative Atomic Mass: 140.9077	**Melting or Fusing Point:** 931°C (1708°F)
Valency: 3	**Boiling Point:** 3512°C (6354°F)
Element Type: Transitional, rare-earth, lanthanide series	**Isotopes:** Most common is ^{141}Pr
	Allotropes: Not known

PRASEODYMIUM is a transitional, rare-earth element from
the lanthanide series. It has a silver-yellow metallic sheen and is
a ductile and malleable substance. It occurs naturally in the
mineral ores monazite and bastnaesite as well as in
trace amounts within the rare-earth metal alloy
didymium. It was discovered in 1885 by
Austrian chemist Carl von Welsbach who
fractioned didymium to separate its
constituent elements. Praseodymium is
used in carbon electrodes for arc lamps. Its
salts, which are green, hence its name, are
used for colouring glass and vitreous enamels
and glazes. The 15 elements of the lanthanide
series are similar to one another, which is why it
took some time to realise that didymium actually
comprised a number of separate elements.

Carl von Welsbach.

Pm Promethium

Promethium, after Prometheus, character in
Greek legend associated with sunlight

Symbol: Pm	**Group:** Transitional **Period:** 6
Atomic Number: 61	**Relative Density:** Not known
Relative Atomic Mass: 145	**Melting or Fusing Point:**
Valency: 3	1080°C (1976°F)
Element Type: Transitional,	**Boiling Point:** 2460°C (4460°F)
rare-earth, lanthanide	**Isotopes:** Most stable is
series	^{145}Pm (half-life 17.7 years)
	Allotropes: Not known

*Trace amounts of
promethium are found in
pitchblende.*

PROMETHIUM is a radioactive,
transitional, rare-earth, metallic
element from the lanthanide
series. It occurs in nature in trace
amounts as a product of fission in
the elements uranium, thorium
and plutonium, and within mineral
ores such as pitchblende. It can be
isolated in this way from spent uranium
fuel in nuclear reactors. It was first
synthesised, and so discovered, by a team led by J. Marinsky
in 1941–47. They achieved it by the particle bombardment
of neodymium and praseodymium. Promethium is used in
phosphorescent paints, hence its name, as Prometheus is said
to have stolen fire from heaven and given it to humans for the
first time. The element is also a source of X-rays. It is also a
component of the nuclear-powered batteries used in spacecraft.

Protactinium   Pa

Protactinium, Greek *proto* (before) and *actinium* (ray maker)

Symbol: Pa
Atomic Number: 91
Relative Atomic Mass:
   231.0381
Valency: 4, 5
Element Type: Transitional,
   rare-earth, actinide series
Group: Transitional
Period: 7

Relative Density: 15.4
Melting or Fusing Point:
   1200°C (2192°F)
Boiling Point: 4000°C
   (7232°F)
Isotopes: Most stable
   is ^{231}Pa (half-life
   32,480 years)
Allotropes: Not known

PROTACTINIUM is a toxic, radioactive, rare-earth element that occurs in trace amounts in nature. The source is uranium ores such as pitchblende. It can be synthesised by the neutron irradiation of thorium nuclei. The element's isotope ^{231}Pa was discovered in 1913 by Polish-born physicist Kasimir Fajans (1887–1975). Isotope ^{234}Pa was discovered in 1917 by the physicists Lise Meitner and Otto Hahn (1879–1968). Protactinium has 14 known isotopes, ^{231}Pa having the longest half-life at 32,480 years. Isotope ^{234}Pa has a half-life of just 1.2 minutes and is a decay product of uranium. The name 'protactinium', which means 'before actinium' was chosen because protactinium decays into actinium.

Lise Meitner (left) and Otto Hahn (right).

Ra

Radium

Radium, after Latin *radius* meaning ray

Symbol: Ra
Atomic Number: 88
Relative Atomic Mass: 226
Valency: 2
Element Type: Metal, alkaline-earth, radioactive
Group: II **Period:** 7

Relative Density: 5.0
Melting or Fusing Point: 700°C (1292°F)
Boiling Point: 1140°C (2084°F)
Isotopes: Most stable is ^{226}Ra (half-life 1622 years)
Allotropes: Not known

Marie Curie's equipment used to measure radioactivity.

RADIUM is a member of the alkaline-earth metals, yet it is highly radioactive and luminescent. It is a soft, whitish metal and occurs in uranium ores or uraninites, such as pitchblende. It was discovered in 1899 by Marie and Pierre Curie. Marie eventually isolated the element in 1911. There are 16 known isotopes of radium, all of which emit radiation in the form of alpha and beta particles and gamma rays. They also luminesce and produce heat. Radium normally decays in stages, producing radon, polonium and then the stable element lead, but isotope ^{223}Ra decays directly to lead by emitting carbon-14.

Radium used to be used in luminescent paints, before the dangers of radiation were fully realised. Many people who regularly came into contact with radium contracted radiation sickness or died from cancer, including Marie Curie herself, who contracted leukaemia. Ironically, radium has also been used in radiotherapy for treating cancers. It works by reducing or even halting the activity of the dividing cancer cells, but it also kills off some healthy cells in the body, which is why there are side effects such as vomiting, diarrhoea and hair loss – the last due to the fact that the cells of hair follicles do not replace themselves as frequently as other body cells. Radioactive cobalt is used more commonly in modern times because it is a high emitter of gamma rays which give a better penetration. Despite the dangers, a great deal of radium has been abandoned in waste dumps over the years, where it is a hazardous contaminant.

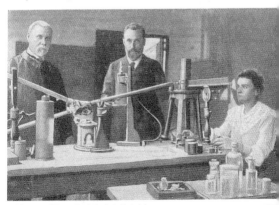

Marie and Pierre Curie in their Paris laboratory.

Rn

Radon

Radon, translates from Latin as 'ray gas'

Symbol: Rn	**Melting or Fusing Point:** -71°C (-95.8°F)
Atomic Number: 86	
Relative Atomic Mass: 222	**Boiling Point:** -61.8°C (-79.24°F)
Valency: 0	
Element Type: Non-metal, gaseous	**Isotopes:** Most stable is ^{222}Rn (half-life 3.82 days)
Group: 0 **Period:** 6	
Relative Density: 9.73	**Allotropes:** Single

RADON is a radioactive, non-metallic, gaseous element.
It is colourless and odourless as it is a member of the noble
gases. There are 20 known isotopes of radon, three of which are
present in the atmosphere in trace amounts. They emit alpha-

Radon is used in the radiotherapy treatment of cancers.

The laboratory of Ernest Rutherford who discovered radon in 1899.

particle radiation but at extremely low levels unless the gas is collected in concentrated amounts. The element was discovered in 1899 by Ernest Rutherford (1871–1937). He named it 'thoron', although what he had actually found was radon isotope ^{220}Rn (half-life 54.5 seconds). Friedrich Dorn (1848–1916) discovered the same isotope in 1900, whilst Sir William Ramsay and R. W. Whytlaw-Gray (1877–1958) managed to isolate the element in 1908. They named it 'niton' before 'radon' was settled on in the 1920s. It is a decay product of thorium, whilst other isotopes are the decay product of radium. Radon is the most dense of the known gases and has been detected in air and spring water having decayed from radioactive deposits.

Although radon is an inert or noble gas, it is not wholly unreactive and has been found to form compounds with fluorine, i.e. fluorides. The main commercial use for radon is in radiotherapy of cancers, as is true of its parent element radium, from which it is a decay product. The cheaper, shorter lived and artificially produced cobalt-60 is more frequently used however.

Re

Rhenium

Rhenium, after Latin *Rhênus* meaning
the German river, the Rhine

Symbol: Re	**Melting or Fusing Point:**
Atomic Number: 75	3180°C (5756°F)
Relative Atomic Mass: 186.2	**Boiling Point:** 5627°C
Valency: 1, 4, 7	(10160°F)
Element Type: Transitional	**Isotopes:** Most common
Group: Transitional **Period:** 6	is ^{187}Re
Relative Density: 21	**Allotropes:** Not known

RHENIUM is a very heavy, transitional metallic element.
It is a silver-white substance with a very high melting point,
the second highest of all the elements. This makes it useful
for alloying with other metallic elements for specialised
applications. The element was discovered in 1925 by German
chemists Walter Noddack (1893–1960),
Ida Tacke (b. 1896) and Otto Berg.
Noddack named the element after the
main river of their homeland, the Rhine.
Rhenium is similar to manganese in
chemical properties and occurs naturally
in the mineral ores of molybdenum and
platinum – from which it is obtained
commercially – though it is the ninth
most scarce element. Its alloys are used
for thermocouples and electrical contacts
where the high temperatures would melt
away other elements.

*The river Rhine in
Germany, after which
rhenium is named.*

Rhodium   Rh

Rhodium, after Greek *rhodon* meaning rose

Symbol: Rh	**Relative Density:** 12.4
Atomic Number: 45	**Melting or Fusing Point:**
Relative Atomic Mass:	1966°C (3571°F)
102.905	**Boiling Point:** 3727°C (6741°F)
Valency: 3	**Isotopes:** Most common
Element Type: Transitional	is ^{103}Rh
Group: Transitional **Period:** 5	**Allotropes:** Not known

RHODIUM is a silver-white, transitional, metallic element. It derives its name from the pink colour of its compounds. The element is very hard, making it a good alloying agent for hardening the elements platinum and palladium. It is one of the elements similar to platinum, exhibiting characteristics such as a resistance to tarnishing and corrosion. Rhodium was discovered in 1803 by British scientist, William Wollaston. It was isolated by the fractioning of osmiridium, the naturally occurring alloy of 'platinum group' metals. Rhodium can be found in the components of jewellery, as an electroplating medium and in thermocouples. Commercially, rhodium is often separated from the residues of the mineral ores of nickel, by electrolysis of the refined slimes, giving pink precipitates.

The name rhodium is derived from the Greek for rose; its compounds are a pink colour.

Rb Rubidium

Rubidium, after Latin *rubidis* meaning 'dark red',
due to its spectrum

Symbol: Rb	**Melting or Fusing Point:**
Atomic Number: 37	38.89°C (102°F)
Relative Atomic Mass: 85.47	**Boiling Point:** 688°C (1270°F)
Valency: 1	**Isotopes:** Most common
Element Type: Metal, alkali	is ^{85}Rb, also ^{87}Rb
Group: I **Period:** 5	radioisotope
Relative Density: 1.53	**Allotropes:** Not known

RUBIDIUM is an alkali metal element. It is soft, silvery-white
and very light. It will sink in water but, like sodium, it is
extremely reactive and will produce its hydroxide. Similarly,
in air it will oxidise very rapidly. The element was discovered in
1861 by German chemists, Robert
Bunsen and Gustav Kirchoff
(1824–87). Rubidium was identified
spectroscopically and its name refers
to prominent red lines in its spectrum.
It is used in photoelectric cells and
types of glass; it was formerly used in
electronic valves. Rubidium naturally
contains a fixed amount of its
radioisotope ^{87}Rb. This decays
into the strontium isotope ^{87}Sr.
A mineral dating technique, called
rubidium–strontium dating, is based
on the extent of this radioactive decay.

*Robert Bunsen, a pioneer
of chemical spectroscopy.*

Ruthenium

Ru

Ruthenium, after Ruthenia, an area in
eastern Europe where it was discovered

Symbol: Ru
Atomic Number: 44
Relative Atomic Mass: 101.07
Valency: 3, 4, 6, 8
Element Type: Transitional
Group: Transitional **Period:** 5
Relative Density: 12.41

Melting or Fusing Point:
2310°C (4190°F)
Boiling Point: 3900°C
(7052°F)
Isotopes: Most common
is ^{102}Ru
Allotropes: Not known

RUTHENIUM is a hard and brittle transitional element, with
a silver-white metallic appearance. Due to its characteristic
resistance to corrosion and tarnishing it is described as one of
the 'platinum group' metals. It occurs as a free or native element
within platinum ores and as a component of the natural
alloy osmiridium. Ruthenium was
discovered in 1827 by scientists from
Ruthenia, now part of the Ukraine.
It was not isolated until *c.* 1844, by the
German chemist Eilhard Mitscherlich
(1794–1863). Ruthenium is used as
an alloying agent to make other
metallic elements harder and more
heat-resistant for use as electrical
contacts, for example. It is also used as
a catalyst in certain chemical processes.
Its compounds are used as pigments in
glass and vitreous glazes and enamels.

*Compounds of
ruthenium are used as
pigments in glass.*

Rf Rutherfordium

Rutherfordium, after Rutherford,
New Zealand-born physicist

Symbol: Rf
Atomic Number: 104
Relative Atomic Mass: 261
Valency: Not known
Element Type: Transitional,
rare-earth, transactinide
series
Group: Transitional **Period:** 7

Relative Density: Not known
Melting or Fusing Point:
Not known
Boiling Point: Not known
Isotopes: Most stable is
^{257}Rf (half-life 3.4 seconds)
Allotropes: Not known

RUTHERFORDIUM is the
name now given to element 104,
although it previously referred
to element 106, which is now
seaborgium. Element 104 also
used to be called 'kurchatovium',
when the Soviets claimed to
have discovered it and named it
in 1969. Then, due to a row

*The laboratory of Nobel Prize
winner, Ernest Rutherford.*

between the USSR and the US, who wanted to call it 'dubnium'
(now element 105) in 1974, it was given the temporary name
'unnilquadium' by the International Union of Pure and Applied
Chemistry. The element eventually earned its present name
in 1994 when its existence was conclusively proven. It was
synthesised by the bombardment of californium-249 with the
nuclei of carbon-12. Rutherfordium has only existed in trace
amounts of a few atoms for short moments of time.

Samarium Sm

Samarium, after samarskite, a mineral named after
Colonel V. E. Samarski, a Russian mine inspector

Symbol: Sm
Atomic Number: 62
Relative Atomic Mass: 150.35
Valency: 2, 3
Element Type: Transitional,
rare-earth, lanthanide
series
Group: Transitional **Period:** 6

Relative Density: 7.52
Melting or Fusing Point:
1072°C (1962°F)
Boiling Point: 1791°C (3256°F)
Isotopes: Most common
is ^{152}Sm
Allotropes: Not known

*Samarium is used as a moderator
in nuclear reactors*

SAMARIUM is a hard, brittle,
grey-white rare-earth element
from the lanthanide series. It
occurs naturally with a wide
distribution, but occurs in
commercially viable quantities
within the mineral ores
monazite and bastnaesite. It was discovered in 1879 by French
chemist Paul Lecoq de Boisbaudran. He identified it
spectroscopically in a sample of the mineral samarskite, from
whence it gets its name. The element has a number of commercial
uses. It is employed industrially as a catalyst in certain organic
chemical reactions. Samarium is also used in carbon arc lamps
and as a moderator in nuclear reactors. Calcium fluoride
crystals treated with samarium have been used in very powerful
lasers, capable of cutting metals. Samarium alloys with cobalt
make very strong permanent magnets.

Sc   Scandium

Scandium, after Scandia in Scandinavia,
where it was discovered

Symbol: Sc	**Melting or Fusing Point:**
Atomic Number: 21	1539°C (2802°F)
Relative Atomic Mass: 44.96	**Boiling Point:** 2832°C
Valency: 3	(5130°F)
Element Type: Transitional	**Isotopes:** Most common
Group: Transitional **Period:** 4	is ^{45}Sc
Relative Density: 2.99	**Allotropes:** Not known

SCANDIUM is a transitional, silver-white, soft metallic element,
in the same group as the lanthanide series, although it is not one
of them. Compounds containing the element are widespread
and common. It is one of the elements predicted to exist by
Dmitri Mendeleyev in 1860, though he used the name
'ekaboron'. Scandium was actually discovered in 1879 by

Swedish physicist Lars Nilson (1840–99)
when he isolated its oxide. Its main mineral
ore is thortveitite. To date scandium has
limited uses commercially. It has been used
as a radioactive tracer in medicine and is
sometimes an ingredient in nickel alkali
storage batteries. It is likely to find a
variety of other applications in the future
as it is almost as light as aluminium, yet it
has a much higher melting point.

*Mendeleyev predicted scandium's existence
in his periodic table.*

Seaborgium Sg

Seaborgium, after US scientist Glenn Seaborg (1912–95)

Symbol: Sg
Atomic Number: 106
Relative Atomic Mass: 263
Valency: Not known
Element Type: Transitional, rare-earth, transactinide group
Group: Transitional **Period:** 7

Relative Density: Not known
Melting or Fusing Point: Not known
Boiling Point: Not known
Isotopes: Most stable is ^{263}Sg (half-life 0.9 seconds)
Allotropes: Not known

Seaborgium was named following Glenn Seaborg's death in 1995.

SEABORGIUM is now the name for radioactive transactinide element 106. 'Seaborgium' *was* the name given to element 104 by the US after 'kurchatovium', 'dubnium' and 'unnilquadium' were all rejected, due to a dispute during the cold war between the US and the Soviet Union. Eventually even 'seaborgium' was rejected for element 104, because Seaborg was still alive at the time, thus breaking a recognised convention that elements can only be named after scientists posthumously. The fall of the Soviet Union brought scientists round a table in the mid 1990s to sort things out. Element 104 was christened 'rutherfordium' having waited longer for a name, and element 106, temporarily 'unnilhexium' was baptised 'seaborgium' after Seaborg's death. Little is known of the properties of seaborgium as yet.

Se

Selenium

Selenium, after Greek *selênê* meaning moon.
Paired with tellurium after Greek *tellus* meaning Earth

Symbol: Se	**Melting or Fusing Point:**
Atomic Number: 34	217°C (422.6°F)
Relative Atomic Mass: 78.96	**Boiling Point:** 684.9°C
Valency: 2, 4, 6	(1265°F)
Element Type: Non-metal	**Isotopes:** Most common
Group: VI **Period:** 4	is ^{80}Se
Relative Density: 4.79	**Allotropes:** Several

SELENIUM is similar to sulphur in having various allotropic forms of the element. The most common allotrope is a grey crystalline solid that is semiconducting. It also has increased electrical conductivity when exposed to light. This means that it is ideally suited for use in photocells, solar cells and xerography or photocopying. This non-metal element was discovered in 1817 by Swedish chemist Jöns Berzelius who named it after the moon due to its similarity to tellurium (named after the Earth), not actually knowing that they would end up adjacent to one another in the same periodic group. Selenium is obtained from sulphide ores and selenide ores. It is one of the essential trace elements in mammalian nutrition, and some reddish compounds are used for colouring glass and enamels.

Selenium was discovered by Berzelius.

Silicon

Si

Silicon, after silica the dioxide of silicon, itself named after Latin *silex* meaning 'hard stone'

Symbol: Si	**Melting or Fusing Point:** 1410°C (2570°F)
Atomic Number: 14	**Boiling Point:** 2355°C (4271°F)
Relative Atomic Mass: 28.08	
Valency: 4	**Isotopes:** Most common is ^{28}Si
Element Type: Metalloid	
Group: IV **Period:** 3	**Allotropes:** Two
Relative Density: 2.33	

SILICON is a brittle metalloid element, existing in two allotropic forms. The more common and familiar allotrope is a crystalline solid with a greyish metallic sheen. There is also an amorphous brown powdery form. Abundant in nature, silicon makes up most of the minerals including quartz, granite and feldspar, as well as the sand that is the product of their erosion. Silicon was discovered in 1824 by Swedish chemist Jöns Berzelius. Processing silicon-based minerals can be a hazardous job. A condition called silicosis can arise from the accumulation of silica, quartz or slate dust in the lungs, where it causes shortness of breath.

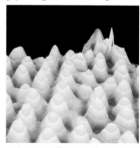

Atoms on a silicon crystal.

Silicon has many commercial uses. Its compounds are used in large quantities in producing glass for buildings. The element is also used in alloys, solar cells and transistors, as it is semi-conducting. Silica or silicon dioxide is the technical name for quartz and sand. Silica gel is an amorphous form of silica which is water absorbent and used for drying gases and oils. Silicates are the salts or esters of silicon, found in many minerals and glass. Silicification is the process by which wood becomes fossilised to become silica. Silicone is the name for a number of synthetic silicon-based polymers, such as the silicone rubbers and gels used for prosthetic implants. Silicon carbide is an extremely hard and heat-resistant compound used as an abrasive and for refractory materials. Silicon chips are tiny slivers of pure silicon with microelectronic circuits etched into their surface.

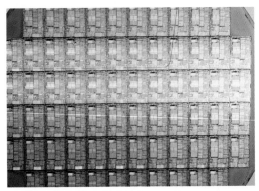

A silicon wafer, used to make silicon chips.

Silver

Ag

Silver, after Old English *siolfor*. Also Indo-European
silubr and Germanic *silber*

Symbol: Ag. Abbreviation for *argent*, Latin for 'silver'	**Period:** 5
Atomic Number: 47	**Relative Density:** 10.5
Relative Atomic Mass: 107.870	**Melting or Fusing Point:** 961.93°C (1763°F)
Valency: 1	**Boiling Point:** 2212°C (4104°F)
Element Type: Transitional	**Isotopes:** Most common is ^{107}Ag
Group: Transitional	**Allotropes:** Not known

SILVER has been known to humanity since antiquity. It is a precious, bright metallic transitional element, which is resistant to corrosion, though it will tarnish in the presence of sulphur compounds. The element occurs as

A specimen of Argentinian silver ore.

a native or free element in the form of nuggets, wires and vein deposits. It also occurs in mineral ores, such as argentine (silver sulphide) and horn silver (silver chloride). Silver is a ductile and malleable element which can be combined with other metallic elements to give very useful alloys. Silver alloys are used for the manufacture of jewellery, tableware, coins and electrical contacts, because silver is also a very efficient conductor of heat and electricity. This also makes it very suitable for electroplating.

Silver has many uses, in both its elemental and compound forms. Silver bromide is a yellowish powder that darkens on exposure to light, so it is widely used in photographic emulsions. The same is true of silver nitrate, which is a white crystalline substance, also used as a medical antiseptic and astringent. Silver chloride, another white crystal, has the same use as silver bromide. Silver is also used in amalgams for fillings in dentistry and in silver solder.

Copper, silver and gold all belong to the same transitional element group, so they have many physical and chemical similarities. Their most important technological role is in electronics due to their good conductivity and unreactiveness. A computer, for example, will contain all three elements as part of its macro- and micro-circuitry.

Silver has been used to make jewellery since antiquity.

Sodium

Na

Sodium, after soda – used to describe
various sodium compounds

Symbol: Na. From Latin
natrium meaning 'natron'
or hydrated sodium
carbonate
Atomic Number: 11
Relative Atomic Mass: 22.99
Valency: 1
Element Type: Metal. Alkali

Group: I **Period:** 3
Relative Density: 0.97
Melting or Fusing Point:
97.81°C (208.05°F)
Boiling Point: 882°C
(1620°F)
Isotopes: Not known
Allotropes: Not known

SODIUM is a soft, wax-like, silver-white, alkali, metal element.
It is a very reactive substance, so it is only found in compounds
in nature. Like other alkali metals it will oxidise rapidly in the
presence of air. Because its density is less than water it will float,
but in doing so it will react violently to produce its hydroxide.
The element is the sixth most abundant on Earth, being found
in many minerals. It was discovered in 1807 by
Sir Humphry Davy. Common salt is the
compound sodium chloride, which is
found in vast quantities in seawater or
brine. Sodium is obtained commercially
by the electrolysis of molten salt, or
through the separation of the chlorine
gas into its constituent parts.

*Sodium was formerly used in the
manufacture of the lead compound used as an
anti-knock ingredient in petrol tetraethyl lead.*

Sodium bicarbonate is used in fire extinguishers.

It is also used in sodium-vapour lamps and for heat transfer in nuclear reactors. Sodium chloride is an essential mineral in the body. Deficiency results in severe muscle cramps and death. Most people, however, consume sufficient quantities through salt added to food as a flavour enhancer. Sodium hydroxide or caustic soda is a corrosive alkali used in the manufacture of soaps and as a cleansing agent. Sodium bicarbonate is baking soda, used in fizzy drinks, soda bread and fire extinguishers. Sodium carbonate is washing soda, used for making soap, glass and again as a cleansing agent. Monosodium glutamate is a white crystalline substance that that can be used to enhance the flavour of proteins in some foods.

Strontium

Sr

Strontium, after Strontian in Scotland,
where it was discovered

Symbol: Sr	**Relative Density:** 2.554
Atomic Number: 38	**Melting or Fusing Point:**
Relative Atomic Mass: 87.62	769°C (1416°F)
Valency: 2	**Boiling Point:** 1384°C (2523°F)
Element Type: Metal,	**Isotopes:** ^{89}Sr and ^{90}Sr (half-
alkaline earth	lives of 25 and 28.1 years)
Group: II **Period:** 5	**Allotropes:** Not known

STRONTIUM is a soft, silvery white, alkaline earth metal element. It is very similar to calcium in chemical and physical properties. It was discovered in 1808 by Sir Humphry Davy. The element is obtained commercially by electrolysis from the mineral ores strontianite and celestine.

Strontium in nuclear fallout causes radiation sickness and cancer.

Strontium-89 and -90 are radioisotopes with a half-lives of 25 and 28.1 years respectively. They are used in nuclear reactors. Both are present in nuclear fallout and are hazardous because they can be absorbed into bone, causing radiation sickness and cancer. Strontium 'units' are used to measure the concentration of ^{89}Sr and ^{90}Sr, in relation to calcium, within substances such as soil and bone. Strontium salts give a characteristic bright red flame when burnt and are used in pyrotechnics and flares.

S

Sulphur

Sulphur (Sulfur in US), after Latin *sulfur*,
also Old French word *soufre*

Symbol: S	**Melting or Fusing Point:**
Atomic Number: 16	112.8°C (235.0°F)
Relative Atomic Mass: 32.064	**Boiling Point:** 444.7°C
Valency: 2, 4, 6	(832.5°F)
Element Type: Non-metal	**Isotopes:** Most common
Group: VI **Period:** 3	is ^{32}S
Relative Density: 2.07	**Allotropes:** Three

Sulphur from the Alberta gas fields in British Columbia.

SULPHUR has been known for many centuries, although it was originally more frequntly called brimstone. It is a non-metallic element and two of the three allotropic forms have a physical appearance of bright yellow brimstone. As well as these rhombic (alpha) and monoclinic (beta) crystalline allotropes, there is also an amorphous, white, powdery sulphur, which lacks any crystalline order. Sulphur burns in air with a blue flame, giving off a pungent odour. Free or native sulphur is found abundantly in volcanic regions, along with metallic and non-metallic compounds. Minerals rich in sulphur include gypsum, pyrite and galena.

Sulphur is used in many different ways as an element and in compounds. Sulphur dioxide, a pungent gas, is used as a sterilising agent and preservative. It is also a waste product of industry and a cause of acid rain pollution (as sulphurous acid), which is responsible for killing plants and animals. Sulphuric acid, or oil of vitriol, is a highly corrosive liquid used in car batteries and for manufacturing fertilisers, explosives, detergents, petrol and dyes. Sulpha drugs are compounds called

Workers extract large pieces of sulphur from volcanic areas in Indonesia.

sulphonamides, used in combating bacterial infections. Sulphonmethane is a compound used to induce hypnosis. Sulphur is also used in the vulcanising process for rubber and in fungicidal compounds. Copper sulphate is used as a mordant, preparing the surfaces of metals in preparation for electroplating and paint spraying. Sulphides are compounds formed where sulphur is the more electronegative of two elements. Many are volatile with unpleasant odours. Hydrogen sulphide is a compound which smells very similar to rotten eggs.

Ta   **Tantalum**

Tantalum, after Tantalus, Greek mythological king

Symbol: Ta	**Relative Density:** 16.6
Atomic Number: 73	**Melting or Fusing Point:**
Relative Atomic Mass:	2996°C (5425°F)
180.948	**Boiling Point:** 5425°C (9797°F)
Valency: 5	**Isotopes:** Most common
Element Type: Transitional	is ^{181}Ta
Group: Transitional **Period:** 6	**Allotropes:** Not known

TANTALUM is a hard, yet ductile, grey-white, transitional metallic element. The element is named after a king from Greek mythology called Tantalus who is said to have deceived the gods by serving them human flesh at a banquet. He was punished by the torment of being kept in the Underworld just out of reach of food and drink. Tantalum is very resistant to corrosion from acids which will attempt to eat away at things, hence the name. The element was discovered in 1802 by Swedish chemist Anders Ekeberg (1767–1813) and eventually isolated in 1820 by fellow Swede, Jöns Berzelius. It is obtained commercially from the complex mineral ore columbite-tantalite, a heavy, brownish substance which also contains niobium and is

Jöns Berzelius successfully isolated tantalum in 1820.

found in course granite. Both elements are rare and highly valued for their properties.

Tantalum can be drawn into thin wire, which remains very tough and heat resistant. This makes it extremely useful for certain electrical applications where heat and vibration are a major concern, such as in the filaments of light bulbs for vehicle lamps. The element is used to make corrosion-resistant alloys for surgical, chemical and dental equipment. Such alloys are also used in rocket engines and in nuclear reactors. Tantalum is also found in rectifiers for capacitors and as a catalyst for the manufacture of synthetic rubbers. Tantalum is grouped with niobium and vanadium on the periodic table. They all have very similar physical and chemical properties, and are used in similar applications.

Tantalum alloys are used in rocket engines.

Tc Technetium

Technetium, after Greek *tekhnetos* meaning 'human-made'

Symbol: Tc	**Melting or Fusing Point:**
Atomic Number: 43	2172°C (3942°F)
Relative Atomic Mass: 97	**Boiling Point:** 4877°C (8811°F)
Valency: 6, 7	**Isotopes:** Most stable is ^{97}Tc
Element Type: Transitional	(half-life 2.6 x 10^6 years),
Group: Transitional **Period:** 5	also ^{99}Tc, plus 14 others
Relative Density: 11.5	**Allotropes:** Not known

TECHNETIUM has the distinction of being the first ever synthesised element. It is a silver-grey, radioactive, transitional metallic element. It was first made by the bombardment of molybdenum with deuterons (nuclei of deuterium atoms), in 1937 by Emilio Segrè (1905–89) and Carlo Perrier. They used a cyclotron and gave the element the name 'masurium', but 'technetium' seemed more appropriate. The cyclotron was invented by Ernest Lawrence. It is a particle accelerator which works in a cyclical rather than linear way. Lawrence worked at producing particles sufficiently energetic for nuclear reactions. Linear accelerators used high voltages and were awkwardly long; Lawrence accelerated particles in a spiral path within a pair of semi conductors mounted in a vacuum between the poles of an electromagnet. Technetium is found as a fission product of uranium and has been detected in stars. ^{99}Tc is used as a radiotherapy tracer.

Early cyclotron designed by Ernest Lawrence.

Tellurium

Te

Tellurium, after Latin *tellus* meaning 'the Earth'

Symbol: Te	**Melting or Fusing Point:** 449.5°C (841.1°F)
Atomic Number: 52	**Boiling Point:** 989.8°C (1814°F)
Relative Atomic Mass: 127.6	
Valency: 2, 4, 6	**Isotopes:** Not known
Element Type: Metalloid	**Allotropes:** Not known
Group: VI **Period:** 5	
Relative Density: 6.24	

Tellurium was discovered in 1782 by Franz Müller.

TELLURIUM is a silver-white, metalloid element with similar properties to the elements selenium and sulphur. It occurs in mineral ores called tellurides, but also in copper ores and in combination with gold in sylvanite. The element is brittle but its strength and hardness can be improved by the addition of trace amounts of lead. The product is suitable for making pipes and sheaths for cables. Tellurium was discovered in 1782 by Austrian chemist Franz Müller (1740–1825), who sent a sample for confirmation to German chemist Martin Klaproth. The element is used in semiconductor devices and as a catalyst for the chemical cracking of petroleum fractions. Some steels contain tellurium, as it increases their ductility. Tellurium compounds are used as a blue-brown vitreous pigment.

Tb

Terbium

Terbium, after a quarry near Ytterby in Sweden

Symbol: Tb	**Group:** Transitional **Period:** 6
Atomic Number: 65	**Relative Density:** 8.234
Relative Atomic Mass: 158.925	**Melting or Fusing Point:** 1360°C (2480°F)
Valency: 3	**Boiling Point:** 3041°C (5506°F)
Element Type: Transitional, rare-earth, lanthanide series	**Isotopes:** Single – ^{159}Tb
	Allotropes: Not known

TERBIUM is one of four elements named after a mineral quarry near Ytterby in Sweden, the other three being erbium, ytterbium and yttrium (not a lanthanide). This is because the quarry yielded the mineral samples in which they were discovered. Terbium itself was discovered in 1843, along with erbium, by Swedish chemist Carl Mosander who detected it as an impurity in yttria, which is yttrium oxide. It was not actually isolated in pure form until towards the end of the twentieth century. The element is a soft, malleable, silver-white, transitional, metallic rare-earth element from the lanthanide series. It is actually soft enough to be cut with a knife. It is obtained commercially from mineral ores such as monazite, gadolinite and apatite. 'Terbium metal' is in fact a term used to describe various lanthanide-series elements – including europium and gadolinium as well as terbium itself – as they each exhibit very similar physical and chemical properties.

Some semiconductor materials contain terbium. A compound called sodium terbium borate is used for lasers. All 15 elements of the lanthanide series are very similar to one another as their electron shell structures are so alike. They, in effect, occupy a single space on the periodic table because they vary so little between lanthanum (element 57) and lutetium (element 71). All rare-earth elements are liable to ignite spontaneously in air – known as pyrophoric – when in an impure sample. Terbium oxide is used as an activator for green phosphors found in the tubes of colour television sets.

Terbium is used as an activator for green phosphors found in the tubes of colour televisions.

Tl   Thallium

Thallium, after Greek *thallos* meaning 'green shoot', referring to the element's spectrum

Symbol: Tl	**Melting or Fusing Point:**
Atomic Number: 81	303.5°C (578.3°F)
Relative Atomic Mass: 204.37	**Boiling Point:** 1457°C
Valency: 1, 3	(2655°F)
Element Type: Metal	**Isotopes:** Most common
Group: III **Period:** 6	is ^{205}Tl
Relative Density: 11.85	**Allotropes:** Not known

THALLIUM is a bluish-white, soft metal. It is highly toxic and its compound, thallium sulphide, is used as a pesticide which pests ingest in bait as it is odourless and tasteless. It was discovered in 1861 by two scientists independently of one another. They were British physicist William Crookes and French chemist Claude Lamy (1820–78). Spectroscopy was used to identify the element, giving rise to its name, as it is characterised by a green line in its signature spectrum. It is obtained commercially as a by-product of smelting the mineral ores of lead and zinc. Some of its compounds are used in the manufacture of both optical and infrared glass. It is also found in infrared detector devices and in electronic components.

William Crookes (left) and Claude Lamy independently discovered thallium.

Thorium

Th

Thorium, after Thor, the Norse god of thunder

Symbol: Th	**Melting or Fusing Point:**
Atomic Number: 90	1750°C (3182°F)
Relative Atomic Mass: 232.04	**Boiling Point:** 4790°C (8654°F)
Valency: 4	**Isotopes:** Most stable
Element Type: Transitional,	is ^{232}Th (half-life
rare-earth, actinide series	1.41×10^{10} years)
Group: Transitional **Period:** 7	**Allotropes:** Not known
Relative Density: 11.72	

THORIUM is a radioactive, rare-earth element from the actinide series. It is silver-white in appearance. It was discovered in 1828 by Swedish chemist Jöns Berzelius. Its chief source is the mineral ore monazite, widely occurring as beach sand. It is also found in the form of the mineral thorite. Thorium oxide, or thoria, is

The primary source of thorium is the mineral ore monazite, found in sand.

a white powder used in incandescent mantles – coverings which emit light when heated. The 'thorium series' is a series of radioactive elements, starting with thorium-232 and ending with lead-208. Thorium is converted into uranium as a nuclear-power source because nuclear fission, or atom splitting, readily occurs in this element. Thorium is one of three such fissile elements, the others being uranium and plutonium. It is additionally used in special alloys and in radiography.

Tm

Thulium

Thulium, after Thule, the most northerly place
in the world according to ancient geographers

Symbol: Tm

Atomic Number: 69

Relative Atomic Mass: 168.93

Valency: 3

Element Type: Transitional,
rare-earth, lanthanide
series

Group: Transitional **Period:** 6

Relative Density: 9.31

Melting or Fusing Point:
1545°C (2813°F)

Boiling Point: 1947°C
(3537°F)

Isotopes: Most stable
is ^{169}Tm

Allotropes: Not known

THULIUM is a rare-earth element from the lanthanide series.
It is silvery-grey, soft, malleable and ductile. It will react with
oxygen and the halogens. It is the rarest of the rare-earth metals,
being found in very small amounts in the mineral ore gadolinite
and similar scarce minerals. It was
discovered in 1879 by Swedish
chemist, Per Cleve. The isotope
thulium-170 is used as an electron
source in portable X-ray machines.
It is created by irradiating thulium-
169 in a nuclear reactor. 'Buttons' of
^{169}Tm are kept in lead casing when not
in use. The thulium is described as
'hot' whilst it emits electrons and is
replaced every few months as it loses
radioactivity. The element is also used
in arc lighting.

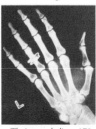

*The isotope thulium-170
is used as an electron source
in portable X-ray machines.*

Tin

Sn

Tin, an Old English word

Symbol: Sn. From Latin *stannum* meaning 'tin'	**Relative Density:** 7.29
Atomic Number: 50	**Melting or Fusing Point:** 232°C (449.6°F)
Relative Atomic Mass: 118.69	**Boiling Point:** 2270°C (4118°F)
Valency: 2, 4	**Isotopes:** Most common is ^{118}Sn
Element Type: Metal	
Group: IV **Period:** 5	**Allotropes:** Three

TIN has been known and worked by man since antiquity. It is a malleable, silver-white metal element. It played an important role in early technologies, being a component in the alloys bronze and pewter. More recently it has been used in the production of cans and other containers, where it is actually a thin coating on top of sheet iron or steel, protecting the metal beneath from corrosion. One source of tin is the mineral ore stannite, which also contains copper and iron. The main source is the mineral ore cassiterite or tinstone, which is tin dioxide – SnO_2. Tin has three

Steel cans coated with tin are protected from corrosion.

allotropic forms that are determined by the temperature at which they form. As well as the familiar silvery metallic form there is a brittle form, above 161°C (321.8°F), and a grey powder form, below 13.2°C (55.8°F).

Tin can be used on its own, or alloyed with lead, to make tinfoil. Tin is sometimes used as a generic name, as tinfoil can be made from aluminium, just as a tin roof is usually made from corrugated iron galvanised with zinc. Tin chloride (II) is used as a chemical reducing agent and for tin-plating by electrolysis. Tin chloride (IV) is furnace-fired onto glass to create an electrically conductive coating. Tin oxide and dioxide, black and white powders respectively, are used in various chemical processes for manufacturing ceramics and cosmetics.

Bronze Age metal workers. Tin is used to make the alloys bronze and pewter.

Titanium

Ti

Titanium, after the Titans, a family
of gods in Greek mythology

Symbol: Ti	**Melting or Fusing Point:**
Atomic Number: 22	1660°C (3020°F)
Relative Atomic Mass: 47.90	**Boiling Point:** 3287°C
Valency: 3, 4	(5949°F)
Element Type: Transitional	**Isotopes:** Most common
Group: Transitional **Period:** 4	is ^{48}Ti
Relative Density: 4.54	**Allotropes:** Not known

A decorative brooch made from titanium, often called a space-age metal.

TITANIUM is a silver-grey, lustrous, lightweight, transitional
metallic element. It is highly resistant to corrosion and
tarnishing, making it a valuable ingredient in alloy steels and
other specialised alloys that combine strength with low weight
and a high melting point. These are used in components in
aircraft, spacecraft and missiles because they will not fail in the
vicinity of combustion-generated heat. The element is quite
common, being found in mineral ores such as ilmenite and
rutile. It was discovered in 1791 by the British mineralogist
William Gregor (1761–1817) and was regarded as an 'exotic'

Corrosion resistant and lightweight, titanium is invaluable for aircraft manufacture.

modern metal. Gregor named the element 'menanchinite' but it received its familiar moniker from German chemist Martin Klaproth in 1795.

Titanium oxide is a white to greyish powder used as a pigment in paints, cosmetics, paper, vitreous glazes and enamels. It also comes in crystalline form as 'titania', a semi-precious gemstone. Titanium will unite with almost every other metallic element, with the notable exceptions of copper and aluminium. Consequently a wide variety of titanium alloys can be made. More specialised uses for these can be found in the field of medicine. Titanium-based 'bones' are commonly used where a patient's real bone has been damaged or weakened beyond natural repair. Titanium plates for patching holes in the skull are commonplace, as are the titanium ball and socket joints for hips and shoulders, as well as titanium pins.

Tungsten

Tungsten, from Swedish *tung sten* meaning 'heavy stone'

Symbol: W. From German name for tungsten, *wolfram*	**Relative Density:** 19.3
	Melting or Fusing Point: 3410°C (6170°F)
Atomic Number: 74	**Boiling Point:** 5660°C (10220°F)
Relative Atomic Mass: 183.85	
Valency: 6	**Isotopes:** Most common is ^{184}W
Element Type: Transitional	
Group: Transitional **Period:** 6	**Allotropes:** Not known

TUNGSTEN is a hard but malleable transitional metallic element with a greyish-white appearance. The combination of its hardness and high melting point make it ideal for making alloys that are used for components that have to cope with heavy wear or high temperatures – usually both. The element was discovered in 1781 by Swedish chemist Carl William Scheele. He gave it the name 'wolfram' which is why the symbol for tungsten is 'W'. It was not isolated, however, until 1783, by two Spanish mineralogists, Don Juan and Don Fausto d'Elhuyer (1755–1833). The chief sources of tungsten are the mineral ores wolframite, hubertite and scheelite.

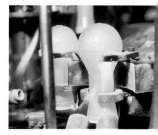

The manufacture of tungsten-filament light bulbs.

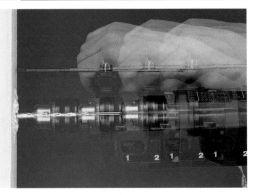

Tungsten carbide is used for high-speed tools, such as the tips of masonry drill bits.

Tungsten has the highest melting point of the metallic elements and will only oxidise at extreme temperatures. Tungsten sulphide is used as a lubricant. Tungsten steels are made from iron with the addition of tungsten, chromium and carbon. Tungsten makes the steel tougher and more elastic, as well as refractory. Tungsten carbide is used for high-speed cutting tools, such as the tips of masonry drill bits. A tungsten lamp has a filament made from tungsten, which is heated by an electric current so that it incandesces. The salts of tungsten are employed in the tanning industries and in the manufacture of paints. Dentists' drills are also tipped with tungsten carbide. They spin at ultra-high speeds to provide a more comfortable and less painful service to the patient.

Uranium

U

Uranium, named after the planet Uranus which
was discovered around the same time

Symbol: U	**Melting or Fusing Point:**
Atomic Number: 92	1132°C (2070°F)
Relative Atomic Mass: 238.03	**Boiling Point:** 3818°C (6904°F)
Valency: 4, 6	**Isotopes:** Most stable is
Element Type: Transitional,	^{238}U (half-life 4.51 x 10^9
rare-earth, actinide series	years), also ^{235}U (half-life
Group: Transitional **Period:** 7	7.13 x 10^8 years)
Relative Density: 19.05	**Allotropes:** Not known

URANIUM is a radioactive, transitional, rare-earth element
from the actinide series. It is hard yet malleable and ductile,
with a silver-white lustre. The term 'transuranic' describes all
the elements with atomic
numbers greater than uranium,
i.e. neptunium at 93 and
onwards. Uranium is used
to synthesise these higher
elements and is therefore the
heaviest naturally occurring
element. It was discovered in
1789 by German chemist
Martin Klaproth. He actually
discovered its oxide and it was
not until 1841 that the element
was isolated by French chemist
Eugène Péligot (1811–90).

*Nuclear fuel rods being loaded
into transport containers.*

Uranium is the most abundant radioactive element, found in various mineral ores, including uraninite or pitchblende, torbernite, autunite and carnonite. The isotope uranium-238 accounts for almost all of the natural uranium, being the most stable with a half-life of just over 4.5 billion years. The 'uranium series' is the set of elements created as uranium undergoes radioactive decay and it ends with lead.

The rare isotope uranium-235 (half-life 713 million years) is one of three fissionable elements, the other two being plutonium and thorium. This means that it will sustain a neutron chain reaction. It is used in nuclear reactors and atom bombs along with plutonium, which is synthesised from

uranium-238. Depleted uranium, with reduced levels of uranuim-235, is used to tip armour-piercing shells, although their safety is now causing concern. Both of these uranium isotopes can also be used for geological dating. The technique is named 'uranium–thorium-lead dating'. Knowing the half-life of the uranium, the age of a mineral can be calculated by the proportion of uranium that has decayed into thorium and then lead. Uranium compounds are poisonous.

Uranium undergoes radioactive decay to become lead (above).

Vanadium

Vanadium, after Vanadis, epithet of the
Norse goddess of love and beauty, Freya

Symbol: V	**Melting or Fusing Point:** 1890°C (3434°F)
Atomic Number: 23	**Boiling Point:** 3380°C (6116°F)
Relative Atomic Mass: 50.94	
Valency: 3, 5	
Element Type: Transitional	**Isotopes:** Most common is ^{51}V
Group: Transitional **Period:** 4	
Relative Density: 6.1	**Allotropes:** Not known

VANADIUM is a silvery-white, transitional, metallic element.
It is a toxic substance. Vanadium was discovered in 1801 by
Spanish mineralogist, Andrés del Rio (1764–1849). He gave
it the name 'erythronium', but remained unconvinced that he
had discovered a new element due to the scepticism of some
fellow scientists. In 1831 vanadium was rediscovered by Swedish
chemist, Nils Sefström (1787–1845) who introduced it to the
world with its present name. The
element is abundant in igneous
rocks and sedimentary deposits. It
is obtained commercially from the
mineral ores of iron, uranium and
lead (vanadinite) as a by-product.
Vanadium is used in steel alloys,
where it provides additional tensile
strength and resistance to heat. The
compound vanadium pentoxide has
various industrial chemical uses.

*Vanadium is obtained from
the mineral ores of lead, such
as galena.*

Xe

Xenon

Xenon, from Greek *xenos* meaning stranger

Symbol: Xe	**Relative Density:** 5.88
Atomic Number: 54	**Melting or Fusing Point:**
Relative Atomic Mass:	-111.9°C (-169.42°F)
131.30	**Boiling Point:** -107.1°C
Valency: 0	(-160.8°F)
Element Type: Gas,	**Isotopes:** Most common
non-metal	is ^{132}Xe
Group: 0 **Period:** 5	**Allotropes:** Single

XENON is a non-metallic noble gaseous element with no odour or colour. It is not, strictly speaking, an inert element for it will form compounds with the element fluorine. Xenon is an extremely rare element. In fact it accounts for just one part in

20 million of air, by volume. It is obtained commercially by the fractional distillation of liquid air. Xenon was discovered in 1898 by Scottish chemists, Sir William Ramsay and Morris Travers. It is used in light bulbs, lasers and arc lamps. It is also found in high-speed photographic flashes. The electrical pulse creates a bright flash as the xenon atoms become electronically excited. It is additionally used in stroboscopes, bubble chambers and bactericidal lamps.

Xenon is used in lasers and strobe lights.

Ytterbium

Yb

Ytterbium, after Ytterby in Sweden

Symbol: Yb	**Relative Density:** 6.97
Atomic Number: 70	**Melting or Fusing Point:** 824°C (1515°F)
Relative Atomic Mass: 173.04	
Valency: 2, 3	**Boiling Point:** 1193°C (2179°F)
Element Type: Transitional, rare-earth, lanthanide series	**Isotopes:** Most common is ^{174}Yb
Group: Transitional **Period:** 6	**Allotropes:** Not known

YTTERBIUM is a transitional, rare-earth element from the lanthanide series. It is a silvery metallic substance, which is soft, ductile and malleable. It is one of four elements named after Ytterby in Sweden, where there is a quarry which yielded the minerals in which they were discovered. The other three are erbium, terbium and yttrium. Ytterbium was thought to have been discovered in 1878 by Swiss chemist, Jean de Marignac. In fact he had isolated an alloy of lutetium and ytterbium. This was revealed in 1907 by French chemist Georges Urbain who initially used the name 'neoytterbium' for ytterbium. Its main commercial source is the mineral ore monazite. Ytterbium is used in the production of special steels, certain alloys and ceramics.

Ytterbium is used in the production of some ceramics.

Y

Yttrium

Yttrium, after Ytterby in Sweden

Symbol: Y	**Melting or Fusing Point:**
Atomic Number: 39	1523°C (2773°F)
Relative Atomic Mass: 88.9	**Boiling Point:** 3337°C
Valency: 3	(6039°F)
Element Type: Transitional	**Isotopes:** Most common
Group: Transitional **Period:** 5	is ^{89}Y
Relative Density: 4.47	**Allotropes:** Not known

YTTRIUM is among four elements named after Ytterby in Sweden. There is a quarry at Ytterby which has yielded the minerals in which each element was discovered. The other three are erbium, terbium and ytterbium. Unlike the others, yttrium is not a member of the lanthanide series of rare-earth elements. However, it is found in the same transitional group as the lanthanides and they are collectively described as the 'yttrium metals' on occasion. It was in fact initially classed as a rare-earth element, but it was subsequently found to have five electron shells, not six. Yttrium is a transitional, silvery, metallic element and was discovered in 1794 by Finnish chemist Johan Gadolin. It was isolated in 1828 by German chemist Friedrich Wohler (1800–82). Its main commercial sources are the mineral ores monazite, bastnaesite and gadolinite.

Yttrium oxide or yttria (not to be confused with ytterbia, the oxide of ytterbium) is used in incandescent mantles. Yttrium is used in alloy steels, where it provides corrosion resistance. It also finds application in the phosphors in colour television tubes and computer picture tubes. Some lasers contain yttrium, as do superconducting ceramics. The Apollo 11 space mission in 1969 brought back some lunar rock samples that have been shown to contain yttrium. Yttrium-90 is a radioactive isotope, or radioisotope, with an interesting medical application. Needles containing the isotope accurately kill pain-transmitting nerves in the spinal chord by irradiation – this technique is far superior to the traditional method of using a surgeon's scalpel to sever them.

Lunar rock samples were found to contain yttrium.

Zn

Zinc

Zinc, from German *zint* meaning point or prong,
as it often appears jagged in the furnace

Symbol: Zn
Atomic Number: 30
Relative Atomic Mass: 65.37
Valency: 2
Element Type: Transitional
Group: Transitional **Period:** 4
Relative Density: 7.133

Melting or Fusing Point:
419.6°C (787.3°F)
Boiling Point: 907°C (1665°F)
Isotopes: Most common
is ^{64}Zn
Allotropes: Not known

Interior of an electrolytic zinc refinery.

ZINC is a bluish-silver,
transitional metallic
element. It is hard and
brittle in pure form but
provides extra toughness
to other metallic elements
in alloys. The element has
been in use since the
Bronze Age when it was
first mixed with copper,
making the alloy brass. It
was discovered to be a separate and new element in 1746 by
German chemist, Andreas Sigismund Marggraf (1709–82).
The earliest known description of zinc comes from the writings
of the Swiss alchemist, Paracelsus (1493–1541). Other zinc-
containing alloys include German silver, gun metal and
phosphor bronze. Zinc alloys have a wide variety of applications.
Zinc is widely used for galvanising iron and steel, which is

carried out by electrolysis to provide protection from corrosion. The main commercial sources for zinc are the mineral ores zinc blende or sphalerite, smithsonite and calamine.

Calamine is a pink powder comprising zinc oxide and ferric oxide, which is used in lotions and ointments for soothing rashes and other skin ailments. Zinc chloride is a white, granular, poisonous compound used as a preservative, embalming agent, solder flux, medical astringent and antiseptic. Zinc sulphate is the compound used in the galvanising process. It is also used as a mordant and preservative. Zinc oxide is a powder used as a white pigment for paints, cosmetics, glass and inks. Zinc ointment, for medical applications, also contains zinc oxide, mixed with petrolatum and paraffin. Zinc sulphide (zinc blende) is a yellow-white solid used for smelting zinc and in the manufacture of fluorescent paints.

A car framework being hot-dip galvanised to increase corrosion resistance.

Zr

Zirconium

Zirconium, from German *zirkon*
via Persian *zargûn*, meaning golden

Symbol: Zr	**Melting or Fusing Point:**
Atomic Number: 40	1852°C (3366°F)
Relative Atomic Mass: 91.22	**Boiling Point:** 4377°C
Valency: 4	(7911°F)
Element Type: Transitional	**Isotopes:** Most common
Group: Transitional **Period:** 5	is ^{90}Zr
Relative Density: 6.51	**Allotropes:** Not known

ZIRCONIUM is a transitional, metallic element. It is a greyish-white lustrous substance and is extremely resistant to corrosion. The mineral zirconia, the element's oxide, was discovered in 1789 by German chemist Martin Klaproth. Zirconium was eventually isolated in 1824 by Swedish chemist, Jöns Berzelius. The semi-precious gemstone zircon is zirconium silicate

Swedish chemist Jöns Berzelius isolated zirconium in 1824.

with varying amounts of contamination, producing a range of colours including clear, green, blue, grey and reddish-brown. Zircalloy is an alloy of zirconium with chromium, nickel and tin. Zirconium is used in nuclear reactors and chemical plants as a protective coating. Zirconium oxide powder is used as a white pigment for paints, as a catalyst, a refractory medium and as an abrasive.

110 (Ununnilium) Uun
111 (Unununium) Uuu

Symbol: Uun and Uuu	**Group:** Transitional **Period:** 7
Atomic Number: 110 and 111	**Relative Density:** Not known
Relative Atomic Mass: 269 and 272	**Melting or Fusing Point:** Not known
Valency: Not known	**Boiling Point:** Not known
Element Type: Transitional, transactinide	**Isotopes:** Not known
	Allotropes: Not known

UNUNNILIUM and unununium are the temporary names given to elements 110 and 111 respectively, by the International Union of Pure and Applied Chemistry. Both are synthetic, transactinide elements and do not exist in nature. Chemically, element 110 is in the same transitional group as nickel, palladium and platinum. Copper, silver and gold are the elements grouped with element 111. Both undergo radioactive decay within fractions of a second, emitting subatomic particles to become lighter elements. This process happens in stages of two, so that the other transactinide elements below elements 110 and 111 will be created in passing. Neither of these two elements has been created in a sufficient quantity to know anything of their physical nature, but they are probably silvery metallic elements.

Unununium is in the same group in the periodic table as gold.

Uub 112 (Ununbium)
Uuq 114 (Ununquadium)

Symbol: Uub and Uuq	**Group:** Transitional **Period:** 7
Atomic Number: 112 and 114	**Relative Density:** Not known
Relative Atomic Mass: 281	**Melting or Fusing Point:**
and 285	Not known
Valency: Not known	**Boiling Point:** Not known
Element Type: Transitional,	**Isotopes:** Not known
transactinide	**Allotropes:** Not known

UNUNBIUM and ununquadium are the temporary names given to elements 112 and 114 respectively, by the International Union of Pure and Applied Chemistry. Both are synthetic, transactinide elements and do not exist in nature. Chemically, element 112 is in the same transitional group as zinc, cadmium and mercury, while element 114 falls beneath a group of metals and metalloids. Both undergo radioactive decay within fractions of a second, emitting subatomic particles to become lighter elements. This process happens in stages of two, so that other transactinide elements below elements 112 and 114 will be created in passing. Odd-numbered element 113 is still missing and scientists are currently working on synthesising element 117 so that it will decay into elements 115 and 113.

Ununbium is in the same group of the periodic table as zinc.

116 (Ununhexium) Uuh
118 (Ununoctium) Uuo

Symbol: Uuh and Uuo	**Group:** Transitional **Period:** 7
Atomic Number: 116 and 118	**Relative Density:** Not known
Relative Atomic Mass: 289 and 293	**Melting or Fusing Point:** Not known
Valency: Not known	**Boiling Point:** Not known
Element Type: Transitional, transactinide	**Isotopes:** Not known
	Allotropes: Not known

UNUNHEXIUM and ununoctium are the temporary names given to elements 116 and 118 respectively, by the International Union of Pure and Applied Chemistry. Both are synthetic, transactinide, elements and do not exist in nature. Chemically, element 116 falls beneath metalloids and non-metals, while 118 falls beneath the noble gases, but nothing is known of their physical properties. Both undergo radioactive decay within fractions of a second, emitting subatomic particles to become lighter elements. This process happens in stages of two, so that the other transactinide elements below elements 116 and 118 will be created in passing, except for missing odd-numbered elements 113, 115 and 117. Synthesis of element 117, which will decay into 115 and 113, is currently being pursued by scientists.

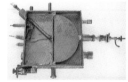

Scientists use equipment, such as this cyclotron, to artificially produce elements.

Glossary

Actinide series All radioactive rare-earth elements similar to actinium, with atomic numbers from 89 (actinium itself) to 103.

Alkaline-earth metal Any of the metals in group II. They are all bivalent and most will react with water to form alkaline hydroxides.

Alkali metal Any of the metals in group I. They are all univalent and will react with water to form alkaline hydroxides.

Allotrope Varieties in physical form of an element, such as ozone and oxygen, diamond and graphite.

Alloy A physically, but not chemically, bonded mixture of metallic elements.

Alpha, beta and gamma radiation Three types of radiation emitted from the nuclei of radioactive atoms.

Amorphous Having no distinct shape or crystalline structure.

Artificial creation or synthesis Manufactured by scientists under laboratory conditions.

Atom All matter is made up of tiny particles called atoms. An atom cannot be split up into anything smaller by chemical means. It is the simplest part of an element. An atom has a nucleus containing protons and neutrons surrounded by orbiting electrons.

Atomic number An element's atomic number is equal to the number of protons in the nucleus of its atoms. No two elements have the same atomic number. Elements are arranged in order of ascending atomic number in the periodic table.

Boiling point When a liquid is heated a point is reached at which the particles gain sufficient energy for the liquid to evaporate. The temperature at which gas bubbles form in the centre of the liquid as well as on the surface is called the boiling point.

Catalyst A chemical that speeds up a chemical reaction without being changed itself at the end of the reaction.

Compound A substance containing atoms of two or more elements.

Electrolysis The extraction of an element from a compound using electricity. Used to obtain an element or to coat (electroplate) materials with the element.

Electron Part of an atom. Electrons occur in shells surrounding the nucleus. They have a mass about 2000 times less than that of protons or neutrons. Electrons carry a negative charge; the negative charge on an electron balances the positive charge on a proton.

Electronegative/electropositive The property of an element, determined by whether it will lose electrons less or more readily than hydrogen, and whether it will oxidise or reduce other elements or compounds.

Electron shell Electrons move in rapid orbits in layers, or shells, around the nucleus of an atom. The number of shells depends on the number of electons the atom contains. Depending on their distance from the nucleus, shells contain different numbers of electrons.

Electroplating The coating of an item with a thin layer of an element by the process of electrolysis.

Element A substance that cannot be divided into simpler substances

by chemical means. A sample will comprise identical atoms.

Fractional distillation The separation of the components of a substance by heating, so that the components (fractions) boil off at different temperatures.

Fusing point When a liquid is cooled the particles lose energy until such a point as they fuse into a fixed poition. The temperature at which a solid is formed is the freezing or fusing point.

Half-life The length of time it takes for half the atoms of a radioactive element to decay. The remaining atoms have a half-life of the same duration.

Halogen Any of the elements in group VII. The name means 'salt producer' as they are all highly reactive.

Hydrous Containing molecules of water.

Ion Incomplete atoms of an element, having lost or gained electrons to achieve eight electrons in their outer shells. Those having lost electrons have a positive charge, whilst those that have gained electrons have a negative charge.

Ion exchange The replacement of the ions (atoms) of an element inside a compound with those of another element, so that the desired element is freed.

Isotope A variety of an element that has the same atomic number, the same chemical properties, but a different atomic mass and different physical properties due to the different number of neutrons in its nuclei.

Lanthanide series All rare-earth elements similar to lanthanum. From atomic number 57 (lanthanum itself) to 71.

Mass number The number of protons plus the number of neutrons in the nucleus of an atom.

Melting point When a solid is heated the particles gain energy until they break free from a fixed position. The temperature at which a solid melts into a liquid is the melting point.

Metal An element that conducts heat and electricity efficiently. It can also be physically bonded with other metals to form alloys.

Metalloid An element which displays properties that are associated with both metals and non-metals.

Mohs Scale Named after Friedrich Mohs (1806–79). A range of hardness in minerals, from the hardest (diamond) at ten to the softest (talc) at one. A mineral can scratch any other with a lower rating.

Molecule Bonds, or links, can be formed between atoms of the same or different elements. Atoms linked in this way are called molecules. For example the smallest particle of water is a molecule containing two hydrogen atoms and one oxygen atom.

Native or free metal A metallic element that occurs naturally in its pure form.

Neutron Uncharged particle that exists in the atomic nuclei of all elements.

Neutron absorber A substance that absorbs the neutrons emitted during nuclear reactions.

Noble gases Any of the gaseous elements in group 0. They were once thought to be totally inert, but will react with some halogens.

Non-metal An element lacking the properties of metals.

Nucleus The centre of an atom, comprised of neutrons and protons. The nucleus takes up a minute part of the whole atom. As the protons are positively charged and the neutrons are neutral the nucleus has an overall positive charge.

Ore A mineral containing a desired element.

Oxidation When a substance gains oxygen or loses hydrogen in a chemical reaction it is oxidised.

Particle accelerator Apparatus designed to accelerate the movement of atomic particles to enable particle bombardment.

Particle bombardment The transformation of atoms by collision with subatomic particles, to achieve new elements.

Patina A surface coating, usually comprising oxides and other basic compounds.

Proton Located in the atomic nuclei of all elements. Protons are positively charged. The number of protons in the nucleus of an atom is an element's atomic number.

Radioactive Able to emit alpha, beta or gamma radiation from atomic nuclei.

Radioactive decay The process by which a radioactive element decays to become another element.

Relative atomic mass (RAM) An element's atomic mass is calculated by comparing it with that of carbon, which has been chosen as the 'standard'. Carbon atoms have a RAM of 12. Carbon is 12 times as heavy as a hydrogen so hydrogen has a RAM of one. As oxygen is 16 times as heavy as carbon it has a RAM of 16.

Rare-earth element An element belonging to the lanthanide or actinide series. They only exist in trace amounts naturally.

Spectroscopy Identification of elements by the distribution and intensity of colour bands in their spectra.

Subatomic particle A particle smaller than an atom, e.g. a proton or a neutron.

Sublimation The process by which a solid vaporises into a gas, without first melting into a liquid, as it is heated.

Transition element An element that is a metal, but has incomplete inner electron shells. The result is variable valency, or combining power, with other elements.

Transuranic elements Elements that have atomic numbers greater than uranium.

Valency Expressed by the number of electrons in the outermost electron shell (valency shell) of the atom. The ability of an element to combine with hydrogen atoms, having just one electron. Some elements have no valency while others may have a variable valency.

Picture Credits

Index

COLLINS GEM
1950s
a mine of information

COLLINS GEM
1960s
a mine of information

COLLINS GEM
1970s
NO GAS
a mine of information

COLLINS GEM
1980s
a mine of information

COLLINS Jane's
CIVIL
AIRCRAFT
a mine of information

COLLINS GEM
CLANS
& Tartans

COLLINS GEM
Classic
TV SERIES
a mine of information

COLLINS Jane's
COMBAT
AIRCRAFT
a mine of information

COLLINS GEM
FIRSTS
a mine of information

COLLINS GEM
GOLF
a mine of information

COLLINS GEM
HILLWALKER'S
Survival Guide
a mine of information

COLLINS GEM
HOME
EMERGENCY GUIDE
a mine of information

COLLINS GEM
Collecting
STAMPS
a mine of information

COLLINS GEM
STARS
a mine of information

COLLINS GEM
SUPERSTITIONS
a mine of information

COLLINS GEM
Using Your
SOFTWARE
a mine of information